The Butterflies' Fly-past

CLIVE SIMSON

The Butterflies' Fly-Past

'Why don't you stop?' 'Why, my dear, only think. If I did,
all the butterflies and cockyoly birds would fly past me,
and then I could catch no more new species...No. Do
the duty which lies nearest you, and catch the first
beetle you come across, is my motto'.

The Water Babies (chapter VIII)
Charles Kingsley

Illustrated by
MANDY SHEPHERD

J. & M. A. WHITAKER
PEREGRINE BOOKS • LEEDS

First published in 1994 by
Peregrine Books
27 Hunger Hills Avenue
Horsforth
Leeds   LS18 5JS

ISBN 0 9520268 2 1

Designed, printed and bound by
SMITH SETTLE
Ilkley Road   Otley   West Yorkshire   LS21 3JP

In memory

of

Maj-Gen C.G. Lipscomb, C.B.E., D.S.O

who

taught me much and bade me

write this

book

Contents

		Page
List of Illustrations		viii
Foreword by Wilson Stephens		ix
Acknowledgements		xiii
Introduction		xv
I	Big Fritz and Little Fritz	1
II	Purple is for Caesar	18
III	A Brown Study	32
IV	Putting on the Ritz	46
V	Birth of the Blues	52
VI	Streaking	73
VII	Buddleia Bugs	83
VIII	All White	94
IX	Skip for Joy	104
Appendix		119
Bibliography		123
Index		125

List of Illustrations

facing page

Silver-washed Fritillary	3
Purple Emperor	20
Swallowtail	49
Adonis Blue	64
Green Hairstreak	74
Peacock	85
Brimstone Parasite	96
Chequered Skipper	110

Foreword

by

WILSON STEPHENS

(Editor of "The Field" from 1951—1977)

We live in an age of unparalleled concern about wild life. Where it is at first hand and well-informed, such concern has great merit, wild life being something about which we should all be concerned. Unfortunately this reservation is decreasingly valid.

Wild life has become the raw material for career structures, politicisation and empire-building to the same extent as has happened to the Health Service and the North Sea oil. The result has been imposition of restrictive practices and erosion of civil liberties under laws which have together constricted previously legitimate freedoms including, as the saddest loss of all, the freedom to enjoy without let or hindrance the pleasures and rewards of the private and unsupervised study of nature.

It is Clive Simson's distinction that he stands as an exemplar (as did Gilbert White of Selborne in the 18th century) of the past naturalists who elevated the fauna of our pastoral and agrarian island into the status of national treasure. They were, as the survivors still are, amateurs in the true sense of that work which is 'lovers of'. They did indeed do for love what the entrenched community of salaried naturalists now does for money. That it is often very handsome money in no way reduces their determination to prevent its spillage outside their own ranks. In short, they are professionals; the likes of Clive Simson are not, and seldom the twain seem destined to meet on any level except that of acrimony.

Like the medieval monasteries, professional naturalists are close to monopolising a national asset. By definition, any monopoly requires a closed shop, which is what the Nature establishment of today has now become. To understand Clice Simson's position, it is necessary to be aware of that other world of Nature to which, happily, he does not belong. He is not alone of course, but the vehemence of the campaign by establishment naturalists against amateurs such as he itself indicates the depth of the establishment's commitment to self-interest in an activity where a high degree of private whim can be disguised as public will.

The mechanics of professionalised monopoly repay study. They begin with the exploitation of that concern for wild life which, as stated, is itself most praiseworthy. However, social changes have resulted in its being fostered, and largely financed, by people to whom the world of Nature is foreign country. Not for them the sunshine and wind and the elusiveness of free creatures; instead of their own eyes, they see Nature through other people's cameras, and read about Nature through other people's words. It is legislated-for by politicians increasingly recruited from (and aspiring to) urban backgrounds. Since the proportion of our population, at all levels, who are directly familiar with fauna and flora is thus progressively diminishing, that originally blameless concern for Nature has become second hand and is having regrettable consequences.

It has called into being a new human element, almost a priesthood — arbitrary, self-protective, exclusive and stipendiary — arrogating to itself suzerainty over Nature in Britain and all that pertains to it. This priesthood has two theocracies in the form of public and private sectors. The former is financed coercively by the taxpayers' money, and the latter voluntarily financed by the wills and bequests of well- wishers who, it need hardly be said, are in no position to influence the ways in which their money is spent. The two sectors are mutually supportive, because of shared interest. Realising that this interest has become a rewarding field of endeavour, in every sense of the term, those of the new priesthood are unwilling to share it.

The consequences of this are that public access to wild life is increasingly by permit only; increasingly subject to official veto, increasingly confined to television and other media, ever more decreasingly at first hand. Instead of participation by direct contact, enthusiasm is limited to second-hand spectatorship. The bogus criterion of 'scientific interest' stands between enthusiastic people and the fulfillment of their enthusiasm. Hence the aridity and joylessness which have rendered obsolete the wonder of personal discovery and now characterise the relationship of man and a Nature which, under pressure of over-population and materialism in our islands, becomes less natural every year.

In this book Clive Simson re-invokes those other traditions of which he is part. The sense of wonder still pervades this old soldier; so does the relish of being successful in the natural world. After a lifetime of ornithology he now turns to what was for long a sub-theme, the butterfly. In many ways the lepidoptera present a more challenging target. Each individual passes through the four different life-forms of ovum, larva, chrysalis, and perfect insect. All of these stages require particular environmental characteristics in order to carry on the chain of life. Therefore butterfly populations are strictly local, sometimes to an area of only a few square yards, and highly vulnerable to changes of land use.

We can all take pleasure in the beauty of butterflies. It may be the chromatic glory of Red Admirals, Peacocks, Painted Ladies, Commas and Tortoiseshells clustering on late summer buddleia; it may be the exquisites of Chalk Downs and Heaths; the familiar company of those sturdy rustics the Gatekeepers and Meadow Browns, and the memories they evoke in each of us who, no matter how briefly, has been a farmer's boy. Or it may be something much more challenging — the subtle gradations of the Hairstreaks, the opulence, usually at tree-top height, of the splendid Purple Emperor.

To detect the presence or narrow the search for any one of them demands the skills of a botanist; a feel for soil and airflows; an awareness of changing weather, and a microscopic eye, all of them exercised separately as the year turns. Every butterfly at every stage is a wonder of creation — as indeed we ourselves are, if freed from the blinkers of 'scientific interest' and the ever-narrowing vista which they permit.

Clive Simson is in that respect most emphatically a free

soul. He will not object to my saying that he is old, as also am I. But age has not changed him, nor custom staled. For him the joys of expeditions and the attainment of an objective enlighten him still. as they did in youth. Few, if any, readers of this book will put it down without having added to what they knew. Who is there, in the free non-institutionalised world, which many of us still contrive to inhabit, whose soul is dead that slumbers, and is not given the kiss of life by this gift of Simsonian gusto and high spirits. Hope is not yet extinct.

Wilson Stephens.

Acknowledgements

I acknowledge, with gratitude, the help given to me by the Rev. Stephen Pittis. He not only proof-read the book, but gave me advice on several matters.

To Jane Errington I am very grateful for her help in arranging my M.S., and for putting it into a suitable state to present to the publishers.

I am indebted to the Editor of The Entomologist Record for his permission to re-print 'The Death of a Butterfly', which I had sent to the Record in 1983.

I acknowledge, with many thanks, advice so readily given to me by Bernard Skinner, whenever I have asked him; and to Jim Porter for kindly sending me an account of the White Admiral, (ab *semi-nigrina*).

To Mrs Helen Brock I owe thanks for her information on *oenanthe*.

To Mandy Shepherd, my daughter-in-law, for her finely executed illustrations.

Finally, I owe much to all those good companions, who have been with me on many butterfly jaunts and jollities.

E. C. L. S.

Introduction

This book is no way a Text Book. There are many such. In my case I started with 'Butterflies shown to the Children' and graduated to Richard South's 'The Butterflies of the British Isles'. The 1921 edition of this book is still a useful Handbook; well written and finely illustrated. For more esoteric details one should turn to 'Butterflies' by E.B. Ford. And there are others; more modern and more expensive.

This book gives a much more personal view. It takes the reader from the Cuillins of Skye to the cliffs of the Wight; from the Broads of East Anglia to the bogs of West Wales. On these journeys I have tried to give the reader some idea of the great variety of habitats of our native butterflies and the pleasure there is to be found in their company.

I have dealt only with our native butterflies, of which there are now fifty-five species. We lost the Black-veined White, *A. crataegi*, in the early 1920's; the Large Copper, *L. dispar,* in 1848; the Mazarine Blue, *C. semiargus,* at Glanville Wootton in 1841; and the Large Tortoiseshell, *N. polychlorus,* in the 1960's. I have included the Large Blue, *M. arion,* because it was only officially declared extinct in U.K. in 1979, and has since been re-introduced. In partial compensation for these losses we have gained a new species, the Mountain Argus, *A. artaxerxes.* Actually, this is only a paper transaction; because the butterfly has always been present in Scotland, but was considered a sub-species of the Brown Argus, *A. agestis.*

So it is about these fifty-five species that I write. My definition of a native species is that it must regularly be present, in some form, throughout the year. I have put a table at the end of the book, showing in what form the various species pass the winter. It also acts as an index; giving a page reference for each species.

In putting the story together I gave some thought as to the order in which each species should be considered. There seemed to me to be no firm rule to follow and so I have pursued a rather biographical path, starting with my schooldays. I have, however, conformed with most views by putting the Skippers *(Hesperiidae)* at the end.

The chapter headings, perhaps a trifle unusual, at least give a clue as to their contents, which are pretty light-hearted. And why not? Butterflies are beautiful; they are fun. They have, in my view, too often been written about in heavy, factual tones. Of course, science demands this. Now try a different approach. Truth is important and all I write of my experiences of rhopaloceral* behaviour in the field is true. But even truth can, surely, be allowed to smile.

I would have liked to have been able to include butterfly visitors to U.K. Some are common; some are rare; a few are very, very rare. I could not, possibly, have managed to have had personal contact with all these. Thus, as this book is based on my personal acquaintance with each species, in the field, visitors have been barred.

Sooner or later the question of collecting butterflies must rear its pretty head. I have no doubt, whatsoever, that a boy or girl can gain both knowledge and excitement from such a pursuit. As they could from birds'-nesting. The latter is now illegal, and for a boy to take a blackbird's egg makes him a criminal. Auberon Waugh, writing his bit in the Daily Telegraph of 1 January 1992, says 'The most oppressive piece of legislation, since children were hung for stealing apples, is the '1981 Wildlife and Countryside Act''. A. Waugh Esq. tends to go 'over the top' from time to time; and his tongue, if not poking out of his mouth, is often in his cheek. In this case, however, he has expressed the feelings of many.

Of course, moderation is the key-word. I do not believe that butterfly-collecting, in moderation, can seriously affect butterfly populations. There is no need for long series of a species, all looking the same, so prevalent in Edwardian times. What is essential is the conservation of habitat and the careful control of chemicals. There is a tendency today for people, mainly townees, to seek to interfere with the pastimes

* Relating to butterflies as opposed to moths.

of country folk. They would appear to find urban sports, such as assaulting old ladies, mugging and car-stealing more acceptable. Many are so bored that they need daily doses of hard drugs to enable them to endure existence. These are the people who would tell us how to live.

They are not the only ones. One sunny day last summer I was idling, net in hand, down a woodland path. Coming towards me, walking their dogs, came two elderly ladies of the 'blue-rinse' kind. Halting in front of me, one, a 'snorting sort', said: 'I trust you are not catching butterflies'. 'No madam' I replied 'only moths'. 'Oh, that's quite alright — just for a moment....don't you know'.

Looking back, perhaps my reply could have been wittier. But we are not all blessed with the brain of the late Lord Birkenhead. As a young man he was having a meal in a restaurant. The usual three-piece band of those days was playing. F.E. Smith, as he then was, was smoking a cigar, when a lady at the next table tapped him with her lorgnette, saying: 'Young man, are you sure you don't mind my eating while you smoke?' Quick as a flash F.E. replied 'Not at all, madam, provided I can hear the band'.*

'Only moths' I had said. In fact, I believe there are certain species of moth far more needful of protection than any of our butterflies. So here I put in a special plea for the Sandhill Rustic, *L. nickerlii leechi* (Goater). This beautiful, silvery moth is found in only one small, sandy Cornish cove and is very vulnerable; unlike the Swallow-tail Butterfly, *machaon,* which recently has been given complete protection. People have 'a thing' about butterflies, unallied either to facts or science. It wants watching.

I suppose any consideration of our native butterflies should mention the Arran Brown, *E. ligea.* Reputedly taken by Sir Patrick Walker on the Isle of Arran in 1804, his two specimens are still in the British Museum. However, do read E.B. Ford's 'Butterflies' for his views on the matter; and an account of an exhibit by T.J. Daley at the British Entomological and Natural History Society meeting of 29 Oct 1977.

*. See 'Great Contemporaries' by Winston Churchill

Personally, I feel that a species that has only been noted three times in 165 years must be so thin on the ground as to lead one seriously to wonder how or if it survives.

BIG FRITZ AND LITTLE FRITZ

Like many other children of my time, I was rewarded for being good by having a fairy tale read to me and pretty grisly most of them were. As I recollect, the tale of Big Claus and Little Claus was well up to the horrific standard set by Messrs Grimm. Presumably their tales were considered the right meat for teutonic 'kinder'. Indeed, much of recent history supports this view. Why the Grimms should have been unloaded on the unsuspecting young of Britain I have never understood: presumably they arrived, along with the Christmas tree and other Germanic symbols, in train of the good Prince Albert. In support of this contention, I must produce the evidence provided by the school to which I went — Wellington. This school was built as a memorial to the Duke of that ilk — 'Nosey' to his incomparable army. It was largely designed by Prince Albert, who much admired the Duke. Perhaps it is truer to say, in the hideous jargon of the present day, that he proposed the 'outline planning'; and this plan was the Prince's ideal of splendid architecture. On the heather wastes of a part of Berkshire, more than a hundred years ago, arose a replica of the Prussian Guard's barracks at Potsdam. Large squares, suitable for drilling Prussian soldiers, were surrounded by long barrack rooms, built over stables. If only the stables had held horses! Actually, they were class-rooms. There it stands today; a wonderful monstrosity, complete with mansard roofs and turrets. It is worth having a look at: its address is Crowthorne.

My morale was slightly up-lifted when, on going to play football against another famous school, Marlborough, I found that a large part of this college had been designed by Britain's top prison-architect. And it showed! It was functional! Once upon a time a commission, appointed by a Labour government, proposed that half the places at these two schools should be paid for by the tax-payer and given to boys from broken homes. Ye Gods; it is only a boy from the most stable home (no pun intended) that could possibly benefit from the rigours of Potsdam. And then the dining-hall; presumably the Prussian grenadiers ate together at battalion strength; at any rate we did. Four hundred boys, in one vast hall, sat down to varied meals. We sat in long tables of thirty seats or more. Certain horrid little boys used to flip pats of margarine, with their knives, on to the high ceiling (whatever modern advertisements may say, you could certainly tell it from butter). There it would drip, in rancid drops, on the diners. The first-day-of-term smell of that hall is with me still. As the days passed, we became inured.

What, you will rightly ask, has all this to do with Fritz? Beyond the fact that Claus and Fritz are obviously related, it has to do with the wonderful country that surrounded my old school. The very Potsdam atmosphere of the school buildings served, admirably, to underline the delights of the heaths and woods, which pressed closely around. I enlisted, aged thirteen, (sorry: I should say passed my Common Entrance) and joined the school at the start of a summer term. I was, and had been from the age of six, intensely interested in birds and butterflies. I had even arrived with a butterfly-net, secreted in my baggage. I was fearful of displaying such an object; though I waved my cricket bat with great bravado. To my delight I soon found one or two boys, older than myself, who were not at all shy of waving a butterfly-net. I eagerly accepted their invitation, one sunny afternoon, to go after Fritz. We were not allowed bicycles and so we had to run. We had to run there and back, to be in time for roll-call and to give us time to chase Fritz. We would run 6 miles: 3 there and 3 back, if necessary. Any stamina, which I may subsequently have shown in the Wellington fifteen, surely stemmed from trying to keep up with my elders on those hot, summer afternoons.

Dear Fritz! We certainly chased him and I have been having fun, doing the same, forty years on. The fact that this is the

Silver-washed Fritillary

title of a rival school's song need not prejudice my loyalty to Wellington. Indeed, if I had gone to Harrow, I should have been suffocated by the bricks and mortar of North London.

So you have guessed the identity of Fritz? Bless you; of course you have. The mention of woods and heaths and sunny, summer days must have given a clue; without the mention of a butterfly-net. Fritz was what we termed the butterflies, known in the vernacular as Fritillaries — genus Argynnis. To us there were big Fritz and little Fritz. We thought more of big Fritz than little Fritz but, much later, I learnt the infinitely superior charms of little Fritz; thus bringing my story into line with Big Claus and Little Claus (you will recall the problem).

Let me go, in much greater detail, into the story of the butterflies known as fritillaries, which are native to the British Isles. There are seven species, which come under this head.

First, the larger members of the breed, in descending order of size:

(a) The Silver-washed Fritillary *(Paphia)*
This fine, big, tiger of a butterfly skims along the glades of oak woods in July sunshine, pausing to sup the nectar from bramble blossoms or to hover momentarily over a dead, brown leaf, in the hope that it might turn out to be a female. The fact is that butterflies have only two ideas, and the other one is food. And why not? They only have a fortnight to live and it is essential that their sons and daughters should parade these glades the following year. To this end their courtship is a delight to behold.

I called the butterfly a 'tiger'. This is because the male has four black stripes on each of his tawny fore-wings. The stripes consist of raised scales, smelling faintly of verbena. These scales are thrown over the female and apparently stimulate her to mate: though the sight of a female playing hard to get does not indicate that she needs all that stimulation! One sees her flying rapidly, with a peculiar winnowing motion of the wings, quite different to normal flight. Close behind is a male and the flight ends high up in the foliage, where mating takes place. A day or two later egg-laying starts and is an intriguing operation to watch. The larvae feed on dog-violets; so the female has to locate a good growth of these: not any old growth, but one within a few feet of an oak-tree. The reason for this will be clear in a moment.

Once I was walking in the Whiteparish woods, in South Wilts, in the forenoon. Paphia males were plentiful, when suddenly I saw a female behaving most peculiarly. She was walking about on the ground and then flying to about 5 feet up on a nearby oak tree. I realised I was watching ovi-positing. The female had found a growth of violets, about 6 feet from an oak tree, and was using her feet to identify the violets. (Butterflies, apparently, use their feet to identify a plant — whether by scent or touch I do not know). Having made sure she had found a good supply of violets, she flew to the oak-tree and laid an egg in a crevice of the bark. I was sure she laid an egg as, through my field-glasses, I saw her arch her abdomen, as butterflies do when egg-laying. This done, she flew back down to the same patch of violets and walked all over them again. Up she flew and laid another egg on the oak tree. I saw her do this five times and each time she had to check the violets were still there! A queer behavioural pattern of which many similar examples occur in the animal kingdom. I saw her lay five eggs on this one tree, all between 4 and 5 feet from the ground. She may have laid some before I first saw her, though I think not. She was flying short distances and walking about when I first saw her, as if searching for the plant.

It might be of interest to follow the future of these eggs and of the tiny larvae which they produce. The larvae hatch in about ten days and at once eat their egg-shells. Having done this they then find a crevice in the bark in which they lie, completely dormant, for 8 months (August—March) when they crawl down the oak and, without a map or a message from Mum*, find a violet leaf. What prodigious stamina; what remarkable acumen!

It is here that I must disagree, for once, with E.B. Ford. He says, on page 102 of his 'Butterflies' (1945), and I quote; 'The

* I may be wrong. Perhaps there is a coded message contained in its genome.

4

Silver-washed Fritillary generally hibernates on the trunk of a tree, to which the young larva makes its way immediately after hatching'. In my view, from personal observation, the larva does not have to make its way to a tree — it hatches on the tree.

Richard South, I hold, is equally wrong, when he writes in his 'Butterflies of the British Isles':- 'The caterpillar hatches in August, and after eating its egg-shell and nibbling a leaf or two of dog-violet goes into hibernation in its second skin.'

In considering Paphia one is at once struck by the occurrence of the female variety *valezina*. It is excessively rare in Britain, except in the New Forest and in certain woods, close by, in Hampshire and Wiltshire. It is a most beautiful insect and inherits this beauty from the male parent, who, himself, shows no trace of it. E.B. Ford considers that 5—15% of New Forest Paphia females are of the form *valezina*. Perhaps I should here explain what she looks like and why, even at my advanced age, I tremble with passion whenever I see her divine form. She is of a dark, olive-green, with an underside of shimmering greenish-silver, shot with mauve and pinkish tints as the light hits it. All this makes it so different that the early fathers of British entomology considered it a separate species and gave it such names as the 'Scarce green Fritillary'.

I have wondered why natural selection has not made the *valezina* form the norm for the species, because it merges most excellently into the dark-green shade of the forest; indeed to try and follow it far is impossible. It would appear to be far better protected than the ordinary colouration allows. I can only suggest that the male, which hunts by sight, has as much trouble as I have in catching the *valezina*, so that mating could be prejudiced. That the male hunts the female by sight is borne out by an old-fashioned method used by Aurelians in the 18th century. This consisted of pinning a 'set' female *paphia* on the foliage beside a ride and using it as bait with which to net the male.

How are you to get to close quarters with this elegant fly? My advice is to choose a warm, sunny day in mid-July and go into a large oak wood where *paphia* is known to fly. There you must patrol the bramble patches, which are in full bloom at this time. Surely you will see many males. It seems to me that the females do not appear, in any numbers, at the feast until about 5.00 pm BST; so save yourself for this magic hour and, if lucky, you may come face to face with the delectable *valezina.*

(b) The High Brown Fritillary *(A. adippe)*
I do not know the origin of this name. The insect is undoubtedly brown, but why is it 'high'? I have looked up the word 'high' in Chambers Dictionary, and, amongst its many meanings, found 'over-excited', 'nervy' and 'difficult'. If you are trying to catch one you will at once realise how well these adjectives fit. All the large fritillaries are strong fliers; but I remember the High Brown as being the swiftest and most elusive. I say 'remember' because, for various reasons no-one can explain, it has largely vanished from its Southern British haunts. The dog-violets, on which it lived, still stand; yet the High Brown no more graces the sun-lit glades. But it still thrives in Northern England and, in 1987, I was delighted to see it flying plentifully in the Cumbrian gardens of the village of Witherslack, and in the woods which closely surround this charming place.

The High Brown flies from late June through July, and its life history differs from the other *Argynnis* species by the fact that the larva over-winters within the egg. Here it lies, fully formed, awaiting its exit in early April. Since the other fritillaries are still to be found, often plentifully, in their ancient haunts, could it be that this ovarian hibernation holds the clue to this insect's disappearance? It is often through such esoteric clues that a mystery is solved.

All that I really know about this dashing fly is contained in a rough note I made over thirty years ago.

'Went with Sam Kirkaldy 26.6.56 to Harewood Forest, Longparish, Hants. A brilliant sunny morning and we arrived at 9.45 am at an open space by the wood filled with dogwood and privet in bloom.

As soon as we arrived we caught a female sunning herself on bare ground. Soon we saw many males dashing about like

Oak Eggars* — scarcely alighting on the dogwood flowers before they were off. By 11.30 am the flight was over and scarcely another was seen, though we stayed till 4.00 pm. By 11.30 am we had caught only nine. Quite the most difficult quarry I have had to chase! All were perfectos. Sam sprained his ankle at the moment of a strike and was a cripple thereafter. The High Brown escaped! On 27.6.56 I started at 8.45 am as we had noticed that early in the morning the insects sunned themselves on the flowers of dogwood and were catchable — later they became far too active to manage. However 10/10 cloud till 11.15 am when the sun came out strongly and stayed all day and suddenly the High Browns appeared from high out of the edges of the wood and I caught two; should have had two more. Within half an hour the flight was over. At 5.00 pm I caught one beautiful female sunning herself on dogwood and one perfect male. I left at 6.00 pm. It appears that if the day is sunny from dawn the insect ceases to fly about 11.30 am. (What happens after this?!). If the morning is dull the insect appears as soon as the sun is *really* strong and flies for an hour. (Then what?). The insects are very arboreal — flying up into the oaks when frightened or when the sun goes in. (Do they mate there?) — yet I saw two males interested in sex — once at another male and once at some dead leaves, which looked remotely like another High Brown, amongst the dogwood. A lot to learn about this chap and the experts know nothing!!'

Note: In the 38 years since this was written perhaps more is known. But I have found that whereas birds are watched throughout their lives, and every detail recorded, much of a butterfly's private life is a mystery.

Before leaving the High Brown it might be of help to give a tip to a beginner wishing to catch and examine a specimen. There used to be places, and probably still are, where this species and the Dark Green Fritillary flew together. Superficially there is a close resemblance, but the High Brown is distinguished, on the underside of the hind-wing, by a row of silver spots each

* *Lasiocampa quercus.*

surrounded by a reddish band. These are readily noticeable and are missing from the Dark Green.

(c) The Dark Green Fritillary (*A aglaia*)

Aptly named for one of the Graces, this species is an inhabitant of open downland, flowery glades and even sea-cliffs, where its strong flight gets full scope. It is out in July and August, but just overlaps with the High Brown.

Its underside, especially that of the larger female, is wonderfully beautiful: large, silvery spots glisten and gleam in the sunshine and seem to serve no purpose but to entrance the human beholder. In watching gorgeous butterflies, or the marvellous exaggerations shown by some orchids, one wonders how natural selection achieved such splendour and to what end. Admittedly, some insects sport gaudy colours to warn predators that they taste unpleasant or sting; but I can find nothing to prove that the pearly markings of the fritillaries indicate an unpleasant taste and they surely carry no sting.

The finest showing of this species that I have seen occurred one sunny afternoon on Salisbury Plain. There, in one of the many grassy hollows, grew many tall thistles. Their purple flowers proved irresistible to the ebullient Dark Green Fritillaries and one could watch and enjoy them as is seldom possible. However, when the female is busy laying her eggs, she can also be closely watched. Once, late in the afternoon on Stockbridge Down in Hampshire, I noticed a very worn female of this species flying slowly, close to the ground. I followed and soon she landed. To my great interest she was ovi-positing in much the same way as I describe for *paphia*; in short, she was walking all over the leaves of the dog-violet and then flying a few feet to lay her eggs deep in the wiry grass that grew in that place. She never laid more than two eggs by the same patch and, like *paphia*, she had to make sure the violets had not disappeared between each laying. It is difficult to account for the fact that the eggs were not laid on the food-plant itself.

I now come to 'Little Fritz' and start with:

(d) The Glanville Fritillary (*M. cinxia*)

This rare butterfly is confined, nowadays, to the Isle of Wight.

In the past it was alleged to have been found all over the place; and was recorded from Tottenham and Dulwich — indeed Petiver called it the 'Dullidge Fritillary'. Morris, in his 'British Butterflies', writes that J.W. Lukis, Esq., took the insect, though rarely, in the neighbourhood of Great Bedwyn and Sarum in Wiltshire. But, then, the ineffable Mr. Lukis also took the Heath Fritillary and the Mazarine Blue, *C. semiargus,* near Great Bedwyn, around the year 1898. If you read Morris you will find many other local species were seen by J.W. Lukis, Esq., 'in the neighbourhood of Great Bedwyn'

I think it is probable that a lot of these records referred to the Marsh Fritillary, which is by no means confined to marshes. After all, the favourite food plant of Cinxia is the sea plantain, *P. lanceolata.*

Before describing my adventures with *cinxia* in the field, the name 'Glanville' should, perhaps, be considered. First, I will tell the story as I heard it. A certain Mrs. Margaret Glanville's will was disputed on the grounds that, at the time she made it, she was not quite right in the head. The Judge, trying the case, asked the Barrister what proof there was of Mrs. Glanville's mental trouble. The Barrister replied 'M'Lud, have you not heard? She collected butterflies'. To his lasting credit the Judge ruled in favour of the will and, later, a butterfly, newly found in Britain, was named 'Glanville' in honour of our first lady lepidopterist. That is the story that I've heard, and it squashed my long held view that the butterfly might first have been found by the famous J.C. Dale, who lived in the parish of Glanville's Wootton in Dorset.

But there are still questions to be asked. First of all, South refers to her as Lady Glanville, from an account by Moses Harris in The Aurelian (1779). Against this, E.B. Ford quotes The Aurelian (1766), in which is mentioned 'the Glanvil Fritillaria'. I don't think this spelling is anything to worry about; after all a generation which could spell Dulwich as Dullidge would not worry about a missing letter or two! But, in only 13 years, the Fritillarias have become the Fritillaries. However, from all this, it is clear that *cinxia* was known to be British before 1766, and that we had a lady butterfly collector sometime before this date.

Now to something of *cinxia* in the field. Today, whatever the alleged distribution was in the 18th century, it is found only on the Isle of Wight. Accordingly, I decided to go there and see this rare butterfly for myself. I went to the Island, alone, on 12 June 1957, in brilliant, sunny weather. I went straight to a steep slope, well inland, where a friend of mine, Dr. Jim Whitby, had told me the insect flew. I had great hopes and was not disappointed. I saw five females, all very worn, and kept one.

In my diary I see that I recorded this as a 'great fact'. (I was quoting Morris's opening paragraph to *cinxia*— 'This butterfly is a very local one, so that its capture must always be regarded as a 'great fact' in the experience of by far the greater number of entomologists.') I saw no males and was obviously far too late for the main emergence. But if there were females there would be eggs, and so I had great hopes for next year.

Accordingly, on 4 June 1958, I went with Jim Whitby to the Isle of Wight. He had spent the night 3/4 June with me at my home in Fyfield, Hampshire, and we left for the Island the next morning. From here-on let me quote my diary:

'Left Fyfield at 06.00 hrs; arrived Portsmouth ferry at 08.00 hrs. Left on car-ferry, in brilliant weather, at 08.30 hrs: arrived Fishbourne 09.30 hrs. Arrived my spot at 10.01 hrs. At 10.11 hrs. set off down the hill (delay of 10 mins due to Jim's frantic efforts to assemble net). At 10.12 hrs. he shouted 'there's one' and wham! he's caught one. Thereafter they came in plenty; just hatched and only able to flop a few paces. Just as well, as I was lame and in pain from a twisted knee. In an hour and a half, rooted to one spot, I caught 19 *cinxia*. Of these I retained 6 males and 2 females. I was, of course, hoping for vars* but found none. Jim scoured the hill-side and was often out of view. He reported the butterfly in numbers all over the area. After a lovely, sunny morning (long to be remembered) had lunch and afterwards, in hot sunshine, tried to locate more colonies on the undercliff round Whitesands Bay. No luck. Understand main colonies on undercliff west of Ventnor. Returned on 16.30 hrs. ferry, still in hot sun. A lovely day.'

* Collectors's term for varieties.

Thirty-six years later I am glad to report that *cinxia* still thrives on the Isle of Wight, though colonies fluctuate in numbers and move around. This is largely due to the fact that the sea-plantain likes recently disturbed soil and so follows the land-slips, on the undercliffs, as they occur.

(e) The Heath Fritillary (*M. athalia*)

This is another extremely local insect, though not so confined as the previous one. In the last century it could be found in Essex in Langham Lodge Wood; in Hartley and Malden Woods near St. Osyth and in woods near Colchester, also in woods in Oxfordshire, Berkshire, Bedfordshire and Sussex. You will not be surprised to learn that the ever watchful J.W. Lukis Esq. found it 'not very uncommonly near Great Bedwyn and Sarum'*. In dealing with the butterflies of Wiltshire (The Macrolepidoptera of Wiltshire, 1962) the Baron de Worms writes that 'it was recorded by the Rev. J.W. Lukis as existing near Gt. Bedwyn (E. Newman, 1869)', but adds the record is distinctly uncertain and even doubtful. I knew the late Baron; a charming man and a very shrewd operator. It took a fast 'shooter' or a very well disguised 'googly' to get past his bat and I don't think the Rev. Lukis was that good a bowler.

The fact is, *athalia* depends on the cow-wheat (*M. pratense*) for its larvae. The cow-wheat, itself, is a semi-parasite and pretty choosy where it grows. Ideally, it likes coppiced areas in woods where it can get the sunlight. As soon as the coppice grows up, the cow-wheat vanishes. Thus it was in those woods where coppicing was regularly done that *athalia* was found. Gradually coppicing became less usual and so the cow-wheat vanished from many woods. It still occurs in North Kent, where there is a requirement for the hop-poles, and here *athalia* flourishes. It is, also, found in Devon and Cornwall at the present time. In these counties the cow-wheat is often present on moors, where it becomes pinkish-mauve instead of yellow, and, occasionally, *athalia* may be found on these moors. I imagine it was from such places that the insect got its name of 'Heath Fritillary'. I, myself, have not taken *athalia* in

* See under *athalia*. Morris's British Butterflies.

11

its Devon haunts, but E.B. Ford (Butterflies — plate 47) shows the Devon form to be darker than the Kentish specimens. *Athalia* has been introduced from Kent into an Essex wood about 1930. Here it did well and from circa 1940 some of this stock was used to re-establish the insect in Abbot's Wood in Sussex, where it existed until about 1925. As Ford points out, it will be extremely interesting to discover if the two 'transplant' insects come to resemble the original Essex and Sussex colonies in size and colouring.

My field knowledge of *athalia* comes from a visit I made with Jim Whitby to Blean Woods, near Canterbury, in 1958. Spurred on by our success with *cinxia*, we at once planned another rapid foray to see another of the rare fritillaries. Dr. Whitby worked at that time in London and so it was decided that I would go by train to Waterloo Station and there be met by him on 23 June. Accordingly I arrived at Waterloo from Andover at 09.42 hours, where Jim met me with his car. Anything less like a butterfly-hunter can not be imagined: there he stood beside a shiny, black car dressed as the complete London doctor — striped trousers, black coat and black velour hat. He laughed off my look of horror; explaining that he had a change of kit in the car and off we set for Blean, via Rochester, in dull, thundery looking weather.

We arrived at Blean at noon and set off on foot to a map-ref given to Jim some years before by a friend. Alas, it was all overgrown. Just then, 35 minutes of heavy rain, hail and thunder occurred. Caught helplessly in the woods, we took what shelter we could; but soon got very wet. At last we were able to return to the car and had a picnic lunch. Then we tried to motor into the woods by various rides, but all were impassable. Eventually we came to the main gate to the woods at Rough Common, and very imposing it looked. It had an arch over the entrance and a lodge beside it, with blue-uniformed attendants. The arch carried the notice 'Property of the Ecclesiastical Commissioners — Private'. We drew back in disarray, until we had the idea that Jim should don once again his London attire — at least the black coat and black velour hat. Thus clad, allied to the imposing black car, we felt he looked sufficiently clerical to pass through the gate, provided I kept a low profile. Accordingly, he drove boldly through the gates and up a long, straight, well tended ride. Woodmen, working beside the road, looked up and respectfully touched their foreheads at the imposing figure.

We continued for about three quarters of a mile, where we found an ideal looking spot consisting of 2 acres of 3-year growth, 2 acres of l-year growth and 1 acre just cut and full of cow-wheat. The weather was still very thundery and overcast and the vegetation very wet; but I decided to have a walk around. Very soon I saw a butterfly asleep on a rush-flower and boxed it. I looked at the underside and there was a diagnostic marking — the beautifully intricate 'leaded-windows', which always remind me of a cathedral. Why such elegance and beauty should have been devised by Nature is hard to determine: it seems to have nothing to do with either natural or sexual selection. Anyway, I had *athalia*, a 'great fact', and hurried to show it to Jim, who was amazed at my good fortune. Several years later, on the Isle of Mull, much the same thing was to happen. I and a companion were after the Slender Scotch Burnet, (*Z. loti)*, and had hunted for it for two days in poor weather. The morning of the third day saw us searching in a new area in drizzle. My companion was high up the mountain side, while I stayed on the road. I was idly looking at some small yellow flowers on a bank beside the road, when I saw a Burnet asleep in the drizzle. It was *loti*. It was blooming luck, but blooming nice!

To return to those damp, Blean Woods. At 15.30 hours the sun at last showed and, within minutes, *athalia* began to fly. I caught 6 just by the car, and Jim, who had gone further afield, had also seen a few. The sun, however, did not last long and, though we stayed for some time, we saw no more. We left at 18.00 hours, arriving Waterloo 20.00 hours. I caught the 21.30 train for Andover and so ended a long day; but we had done the *cinxia-athalia* double within 3 weeks and had found them both at the exact time of emergence. Thus the few we took were at their most perfect and beautiful.

(f) The Marsh Fritillary (*E. aurinia)*
Old Morris calls this butterfly the Dishcloth, or Greasy Fritillary.

The modern vernacular name — Marsh — is somewhat misleading, whereas 'greasy' exactly describes the underside appearance. Misleading, because a marsh is by no means the first place I would search for *aurinia.* I would try and find a place where the Devil's-bit, Scabious, (*S. succissa),* grew in profusion and this could well be on a dry, chalk hill or a grassy slope on Salisbury Plain, say. Indeed, there are colonies of *aurinia* all over the Plain. They move around, and I have found the Narrow-bordered Bee Hawk, (*H. tityus),* sometimes to be of their number.

My first sight of *aurinia* was in 1955, when it fairly swarmed on St. Catherine's Mount, near Winchester. There it flew, in late May, with the Adonis Blue, and the pair made a sight to thrill the heart of a countryman. They only lasted here for another 3 years, because the place became overgrown and the Devil's-bit, along with the Horse-shoe Vetch, (*H. comosa),* found it impossible to thrive.

This is probably the story of *aurinia* throughout its range in the British Isles. But its caterpillars are heavily preyed on by a Hymenopterous parasite called *Apanteles,* which acts as a useful control. Without such control the following extract from South's 'Butterflies of the British Isles' shows what can happen:- 'This butterfly *aurinia* has been known to increase so prodigiously that whole fields and roads became blackened by the moving myriads of larvae'.

The whole question of the natural controls of insects is of great interest, for without them there would hardly be a green leaf left in Britain. Just consider how a swarm of locusts leaves not a living bit of vegetation behind it. In Britain the controls consists of parasites such as ichneumons, braconids and tachenids, which, between them, prey upon the ova, larvae and pupae of other insects, which feed on vegetation. The birds take a tremendous toll of larva and imago; while bats prey solely on imagines. In all cases, where a proper balance of nature is achieved, the victim benefits as much as the attacker. For instance, in the case quoted from South above, the resultant imago were 'extremely small and faded in colour'. Also, in Canada, steps were taken to protect the caribou herds from the wolves, which preyed upon them. The result was the reverse of what had been hoped: the caribou declined in numbers. It was found that the wolves largely destroyed the very old and the sickly amongst the herds, and that this assisted the well being of the caribou. Whilst on this subject, it has been stated that, from time to time, a certain species of butterfly or moth had become extinct in a region due to parasites. Though this may happen very locally, it is true to say that, in general, a species can not be utterly destroyed by another species which lives upon it. Thus, the last tiger in an Indian forest will die of starvation before it kills the last sambur, which is its staple diet. The whole thing, known as the 'balance of nature', is designed for the benefit of all creatures: it is only man who upsets it, often with disastrous results.

(g) The Pearl-bordered *(B. euphrosyne)* and Small Pearl-bordered *(B. selene)* Fritillaries

I have lumped these two species together. They frequent similar places; their larvae feed on the same pabulum — dog-violet — and they were both common species. *Euphrosyne** is the first to emerge; showing up about mid-May and flying in woodland clearings, where the violets grow in plenty. Why it was originally called 'The April Fritillary' I do not know. Either the springs long ago were much warmer, or it was mistakenly identified. It may be due to the change in the calendar, when dates were put forward by eleven days. 'Give us back our eleven days', cried the people, rioting all over the place, as is the wont of the feeble minded. But pretty *euphrosyne* did not riot, and she still emerges when the sun has reached a certain height, whatever man may call the date.

Her sister, *selene*, should be looked for the first week in June. I first saw this butterfly in abundance on 3 June '56, flying with the rare Wood White, in a wood in Surrey. It swarmed along the sedgy, rather damp rides, which traversed this wood. I have since found that similar rides are likely to produce it all over the country. In 1987 I was delighted to see it, in numbers, in Cumbria.

* *Euphrosyne* is currently contracting its range.

This butterfly is readily distinguished in the field from *euphrosyne* by the deep, chocolate coloured markings on its underside. It is very variable, as are all the Fritillaries, and there are those who find excitement and not a little joy in hunting for these rare aberrations. It is hard work and means spending long hours patrolling the woodland rides and those patches of flowers and blossoms being most in favour by a particular species. Such a one was the late Maj-gen. C.G. Lipscomb, whose butterfly collection, now in the British Museum (Natural History), contained some remarkable varieties. They were often very beautiful and I thought the strange alterations to the normal underside patterns to be particularly wonderful. One of Gen. Lipscomb's favourite places for Fritillaries was Grovely Wood, on the southern edge of the great Salisbury Plain. Here he spent many golden, summer hours waiting and watching for the moment when one of these rarities was to appear. Just how patient Lippy (for that was how his friends knew him) must have been becomes apparent when one considers one's own experience in the field. Of all the multitude of Fritillaries seen, how many spectacular aberrations were noted? In my case — none; yet he had many.

(h) The Duke of Burgundy Fritillary (*H. lucina*)

Although not a Fritillary, I can not resist including this charming little butterfly among the Frits. First of all it much resembles the fritillary pattern (originally named from the butterflies' supposed resemblance to the flower fritillaria). Secondly, it has a name full of distinction and romance. Thirdly, when I was a young boy I longed, nay yearned, to add this noble insect to my little storebox collection of butterflies, which included, I may say, the now so rare Large Tortoiseshell. Back in those days it was not uncommon.

I read all I could about the 'Duke'; how the male had only four legs, though the female had six! How the wing shapes of the two sexes differed quite markedly. Above all, how it darted about the sunlit glades and paths of open woodland at the loveliest time of the year — the last days of May and early June. Unfortunately, I was always at school at this time and, as my schools seemed to be entirely surrounded by acid soils and rhododendrons, it was not surprising that I had to wait a long time before I saw my first real, live Duke of Burgundy. In fact, I was fifty years old when I saw and caught my first one.

I must not give the impression that, since leaving school at the age of eighteen, I had, haggard and gaunt, endlessly searched the woodland glades in early summer for this prize: far from it. Indeed, I joined the army and saw the world, and never a thought gave I to little English butterflies; though I did gaze in awe at certain enormous, gaudy varieties in the tropics. But, as the day of my retirement drew near, I thought that I might just make a hobby out of butterfly-collecting. It seemed to offer opportunities to explore some of the loveliest countryside at the most pleasant times of the year. Travel over Britain would also be necessary: from 3,000 ft. plus in the Highlands to zero feet on the Isle of Wight. (I was thinking of the Mountain Ringlet and the Glanville Fritillary).

My last army job was as a president at the War-Office Selection Board at Barton Stacey, in the county of Hampshire. And here, one warm noon-tide in early June, I thought I would have another look at one of the team-obstacles, which seemed to be causing the candidates some trouble. Standing there, thinking how there must be a simple way to tackle this obstacle, I saw my very first, real, live Duke of Burgundy. It was sunning itself on the leaf of a near-by bush. Whipping off my uniform cap, and showing remarkable speed and agility for one of my rank and age, I caught the butterfly in my cap. That the cap sported a red flannel band was only appropriate for a butterfly of such distinguished nobility!

In subsequent years, in the woods round Winchester and Andover, and, quite often, on the open grasslands of Salisbury Plain, I was to see this butterfly in plenty; indeed, wherever cowslips grew. I remember once, at a picnic, introducing a small son to the butterfly. He was thrilled, because he apparently thought it was called the 'Duke of Edinburgh' and, perhaps, there might be some award!

PURPLE IS FOR CAESAR

'And if there be one branch of Natural History which is to me more captivatingly interesting than another, it is Entomology; one which is moreover so easy of full gratification, so compatible with every pursuit, so productive of friendly feelings with others, so amalgative of the high and low together in perfect amity, so singularly pleasing and delightful in itself'. Thus, over 100 years ago, wrote the Rev. F.O. Morris, for 40 years vicar of Nunburnholme, Yorkshire.

Beyond the charm of his English lies his deliciously unscientific approach: so different from modern publications on Natural History. In much the same spirit the writer, retiring some years ago, looked for something so easy of full gratification and so captivatingly interesting. Up to a point there were moments of easy gratification. Lustrous, hitherto seemingly unattainable, butterflies fluttered in the net. Yet always the incomparable, the superb Purple Emperor *A. iris* eluded not only the net, but even the wistful gaze, of the ageing Entomologist. Wistful may be considered an odd word to use for such a 'singularly pleasing' pursuit. But if one stands in lonely, woodland rides in July, year after year, with puckered eyes glued to the tops of tall oak trees: if one loiters to windward of a very dead rabbit for hours on end or paces beside a white sheet spread on the forest floor, all without success, one's gaze indubitably becomes, in time, wistful — very wistful. And the years creep by. (The rabbit and the white sheet are well known methods of attracting the Emperor from the top of his oak tree. The writer is, therefore, no madder than a fisherman).

However, on the 23rd July, the wistful gaze turned to open-eyed amazement and then rapidly, through stages of steely-eyed determination, to mellow gratification. Yes, a Purple Emperor was seen, watched and bagged in a matter of seconds. It happened like this. On arriving by car, in a large oak wood in South West England, two fellow Emperor-hunters were seen. No brash schoolboys these, but grave, elderly and courteous, with much knowledge of the Emperor and his ways. Trusting that old Morris was right in saying the pursuit was 'productive of friendly feelings with others', the writer asked if he might park his car in the same glade as theirs. More in bravado than in hope, he took his net in hand and stood beside his new friends — an 'amalgamation of the high and low together with perfect amity'; or so he hoped. Because they were undoubtedly high in both knowledge and hope. The writer was low in both. He listened, enthralled, to their reminiscences and then asked 'If we do see one, does it go to the fleetest of foot; or what?' Answer came there none because, at that very moment, with a rustle and a flutter, with a glide and a glint of purple, his Imperial Majesty landed, plump, on the door of the most aristocratic of the cars in the glade. It happened to be mine. 'Your bird' said one of the wise men and, under the awful gaze of two such accomplished entomologists, the writer did a sort of rustic 'cowshot' to mid-wicket and found the gleaming prize in his net. It was pronounced a perfect specimen, newly emerged. The writer expressed, perhaps too enthusiastically and boyishly, his pleasure and thanks. Anyway, the two sages walked rapidly away down the ride, their shoulders shaking. The sight of bald head and heavy limbs doing a war-dance over the purple fly had been too much for them.

A day or two later luck was tried again. A curious mixture of thrill and exasperation followed. Within minutes a Purple Emperor descended to inspect the sheet laid out for his curiosity. He fluttered slowly around and then sat, fanning his glorious wings, on the tip of a fir-bough, about 10 ft. up. The writer approached, made a lumbrous leap in the air, and gave what he fondly hoped was a Wimbledon smash with the net. He missed by a whisker. And then a countryman came down the lane. He asked 'Are you looking for a large butterfly with blue wings? If so, I have one at my farm at the edge of the wood'. There, sure enough, was an Emperor. He was imprisoned in a jam jar, with a lot of loose clover heads. He had been injudicious enough to land, at 7.30 that morning, on the white path of the farm garden. He had allowed himself to be caught in a handkerchief! Another had landed, a little later, on the farm-wife's apron, as she hung out the washing. The captive was useless as a specimen, being much dishevelled; but he rode on the finger, during the walk through the woods, until he felt strong and refreshed. Then he mounted, with great speed, to disappear amongst the highest oaks. The feel of his strong feet and the winnowing of his wings was a delight. Altogether six Emperors were seen up to midday — all inaccessible.

This short account sums up the experience of many people with this most magnificent of our native insects. Long periods of fruitless waiting and searching: then he takes pity and.....well, the matter becomes, as in the words of Morris, 'captivatingly interesting'.

All this was written many years ago, while I was still, so to speak, hot from the chase. I tried many more times to catch the imago. My first success I have already recounted; my second was a little more elaborate. The date was 31st July 1965 — the place; Whiteparish. At last the weather, after 14 days of heavy cloud and rain, had become sunny and so I decided on a morning after *iris*.

I parked my car in a little lay-by in a lane which ran through the woods and at once saw a male *iris* flying round the top of an oak tree. I watched him for some time and saw him dash at about six male Purple Hairstreaks, who were skirmishing in a small bunch round the top of the oak. They scattered in all directions and did not reform. Once he set off after a wood-pigeon, which flew close to his chosen tree!

But he spent most of his time walking about the upper trunk of the tree, apparently seeking some nutriment. I spread a white sheet on the road and added some bright, silver paper. I had heard that this sort of thing sometimes attracted the male *iris*. Today, they held no attraction. And then I saw a small mounted posse approaching. Hastily

Purple Emperor

grabbing up my sheet, I saw a thin, gnarled woman on a horse leading a string of 5 little girls on 5 little, fat ponies. To the woodland gods I prayed — let just one pony drop some fresh dung. (The male *iris* is partial to this. A friend of mine, in Sussex, finds the noisome effluent from a piggery very attractive to *iris*).

You'll not believe this but, cross my heart, one little fat pony, at this moment, decided to do its morning business. It stopped and, paying no attention to the frantic kickings of its little passenger, deposited a fine pile of manure bang in the middle of the road. Who dare say that the woodland gods have lost their power?

I sat in my car and watched that pile for an hour. No joy. So I set off down the lane towards another, hopeful area. A car came fast towards me and ran over a Purple Emperor before my eyes. The beautiful creature was on the road and was sucked up under the car. It was left, on the road, a mangled wreck with one antenna twitching! After hunting for *valezina* (the beautiful, green form of the Silver-washed Fritillary) amongst the brambles, and netting one, I returned to my original pitch. As I approached the pile of dung I saw, incredibly, a male *iris* sitting on it and fanning his glorious purple at me. I was almost on top of the insect but, seizing my net from the back seat, I opened the door and made an instant strike with the net. The dung flew about, but *iris* was captive. A perfect male and my hands were trembling as I boxed it.

I showed it to lovely May Yellowlees (the owner of the Whiteparish pub); had bread and cheese and a pint of ale, and sped off home to meet some friends who wanted to see the White-letter Hairstreak in Harewood Forest. By tea-time we had seen 7. Those were the days!

To be more accurate; those were the days before I was taught how to find the eggs of the Purple Emperor and, learning from one's mistakes, to rear the insect to maturity.

I was taught by a friend, the late Maj-Gen. C.G. Lipscomb, where and how to look for the eggs. Before he had perfected this art, he had spent much time doing what most people do when trying to catch *iris* — hanging about woodland rides in the early morning of a sunny July day; or sitting besides the rotting corpse of a rabbit, or a game-keeper's gibbet. In his determination to obtain a short series of this noble fly he had once obtained a horse's head from the local knackers. He let it ripen for a bit at the bottom of his garden and then, wrapped in a sack, put it in the boot of his car. Thus burdened, he set off for the woods at Whiteparish in South Wiltshire. To get there he had to go through Salisbury and, of course, his speed became considerably reduced. It was not long before he realised that he had one or two dogs cantering along behind his car, showing great interest in the boot. Soon he had a fair imitation of the V.W.H. (Cricklade) pack, in numbers if not quality, at heel. Unlike a well behaved pack of hounds, his following must have contained some 'lager louts', because fights broke out with distressing frequency, causing traffic problems of various kinds and arousing the considerable interest of the citizens of Sarum. The General became most embarrassed, knowing that to stop and jettison the sack would cause the biggest dog fight ever recorded in Wiltshire, together with other unseemly sights. If he was to speed up the car he would add a speed-cop or two to his already troublesome tail. There was nothing for it, but to 'press on regardless' until the streets of Salisbury gave way to the open country and he could accelerate beyond the speed of the fleetest dog.

So this he did, suffering the pointed fingers of the populace and with the frantic cries and whistles of various dog-owners ringing in his ears. He told me that, even after he had cleared the town, two long-dogs raced behind him for a while.

The General, as a Lieut-Colonel, had commanded a battalion of the Somerset Light Infantry in Normandy through to Germany. For this he had received a DSO and a bar. He told me that he was more troubled that time in Salisbury than ever he had been in France!

However, to return to our muttons — or rather our horse's head. My friend duly arrived at the glade he had previously selected and hung up the bait. He rubbed his hands in glee; surely no *iris* could resist this feast. He sat, up-wind, through the hours of the so-called morning-flight: he sat through till the close of the so-called evening flight. No *iris*. Then he took

22

his spade and he buried his horse's-head many feet deep. Never again did he attempt this method of catching *iris*.

Instead, he learnt how to find *iris'* eggs and was kind enough to instruct me. Now, at no further charge, I shall pass on the esoteric skills required to you. This not only covers the actual finding of an egg, without which nothing will happen, but also the various moments of crisis, which occur during the 11 months and 10 days or so whilst the insect is reared to maturity, and is your sole responsibility.

Eggs are laid chiefly on *Salix caprea* (The Pussy Willow) in Britain. Occasionally they have been found on the Eared Sallow (*S. aurita*) and, on the Continent, on Willow *(S.fragilis)*. Personally, I have only searched Pussy Willows. These grow plentifully in the woods occupied by *iris* and, though occasionally growing over 15 ft. tall, are usually shorter and quite manageable with the handle of a walking stick. There is no doubt that bushes standing about a woodland ride, or those in open glades, are most favoured for egg-laying. The eggs are laid on the upper surface of a leaf; usually close to the mid-rib, but can be far out towards the edge. The chosen leaf can be anywhere — in the centre of the bush or towards the edge. They can be chest high or out of reach at the top of a tall bush. Once, when I was egg-hunting, a female *iris*, black and monstrous big, swept in and laid two eggs in the middle of a large bush across the ride from me. I watched as she walked about and saw her suddenly arch her abdomen and lay an egg on the top of a leaf. She then fluttered a few feet and laid a second egg. I had had no luck that day and was thrilled at this gift of two eggs. The time was 16.00 hours, during the only sunny spell (10 minutes) of the whole afternoon.

I had previously read, in a book by F.W. Frohawk, how the workers in his local woods used to describe the female *iris* as 'striking the bushes' when she went a-laying. Now I had seen this for myself. I was, also, sufficiently near as to be able closely to observe exactly what went on within the bush: I quote from my diary: 'She fluttered about, landed on a leaf and, facing towards the stem, shuffled forward and depressed her abdomen until the tip touched the leaf. She seemed to require to feel the leaf-stem. On a large leaf one would, therefore, expect to find the egg nearer the stem than the tip'.

In this instance two eggs were laid, and I believe this to be normal practice. However, in a previous year I was lucky enough to watch a female lay what I believe to have been five eggs. This happened in a very tall bush and I was unable to reach the area where the laying occurred. In this case the female, halfway through, flew out of the bush and took one or two turns round the bush before returning right into the heart of the foliage. I am pretty certain that, in all, five eggs were laid before the butterfly left and flew swiftly up and away.

I think it is now appropriate to describe the egg. When newly laid it is a bright, apple-green. It is vertically ribbed and has a ring at the base, where it is gummed to the leaf. The first colour change in a fertile egg occurs in the basal ring, which slowly turns black. Gradually, the whole egg changes colour until, just before hatching, it is almost black. The normal hatching time is 13 days, occasionally 12 or 14.

The egg is always laid on the top of a leaf and the larva also lives on top of the leaf. The larva, when first hatched, has a black head and a pale body ending in a point. The head appears far too large for the body, and has no horns. It immediately takes up a position on a leaf with its tail at the tip and the head down the mid-rib. Even so young it makes a small, silken pad on which to rest, and, throughout its life, will never move away from a pad without leaving a silken thread to guide itself back.

I feel that, having talked about the egg and the first instar larva, the best way forward is by means of two tables; Table A and Table B. The first deals with the finding of ova during the period 1965-1986; the second is a diary of events in the life of *iris* from ova to imago, with explanatory notes.

Thus, the two Tables follow and this chapter ends.

TABLE A

					RECORD OF IRIS OVA FOUND BETWEEN 1965 & 1986
Ser No.	Year	Date	Ova	Place	Remarks
1	1965	3 Aug	12	Whiteparish, Wilts	In the company of Gen. Lipscomb, who showed me how to find them. 10 on one bush.
2	1966	18 July 28 July	2 1	Do Do	Very early. About to hatch.
3	1967	16 July 3 Aug	1 2	Do Do	Very early. Fresh. About to hatch.
4	1968	11 Aug	5	Do	3 different,♀s as 2 were black; 2 grey and 1 green.
5	1969	16 July 25 July 26 July 4 Aug	- 2 2 1	Do Do Do Do	♀ seen laying 5 eggs out of reach.
6	1970	20 July	2	Do	♀ seen laying on bush. 2 eggs taken. Eggs hatched 1 Aug=12 days incubation.
7	1971	25 July	4	Do	2 fresh eggs on same leaf; first occurrence. Remaining 2 on same bush, but not fresh. Fresh pair hatched 6 Aug=13 days incubation.
8	1972	14 Aug	3	Do	Went 3 Aug. Found none. A very late year for Iris. On 14 Aug found 3 eggs after 5 hours searching.
9	1973	20 July	4	Do	All found on same bush but from 2♀s as incubation different.
10	1974		zero	Do	3 visits. No imago seen; no ova found.
11	1975	31 July	2	Do	On same bush as for Ser.9.
12	1976	22 July	3	Do	Also one larva in 2nd instar. Ova must have been laid 28 June. Very early.
13	1979	1 Aug	3	Do	Wood much cut about and favourite bushes gone or grown too tall. 1 ova grey; 2 fresh on bush at edge of wood.
14	1980	1 Aug	6	Do	Found a new area with young sallows.
15	1983	2 Aug	1	Winchester, Hants	New area & hard work to find a good bush. Missed 1 ova!
16	1986	1 Aug	3	Oxfordshire	1 hatched 15/8=14 days. 1 hatched 4/8 & 1 infertile.

TOTAL = 59 OVER 11 YEAR PERIOD

DIARY OF EVENTS IN THE LIFE OF A PURPLE EMPEROR FROM OVA TO IMAGO*

Ser No.	Date	Event	Remarks
1	20 July 1970	Egg laid 16.00 hrs	I witnessed the laying of 2 eggs (See note A).
2	1 Aug	Egg hatched (after 12 days)	At 15.05 hrs. I saw black head poking out of shell.
3	12 Aug	First skin change (11 days after birth)	Whole appearance now much changed, with two horns, a yellow shoulder stripe & a pointed tail. (See note B).
4	1 Sep	Second skin change (31 days after birth).	This skin is to last right through to next Spring. There is very little growth. (See note C).
5	5 Nov	Larva started to turn brown.	In preparation for hibernation.
6	10 Nov	Larva left leaf for hibernation.	
7	15 Nov	Pad completed and larva comatose by this date.	(See note D)
8	10 April 1971	Left pad and took up position at base of a leaf-bud	This was the day the Brimstones (G.rhamni) flew in my garden. Sallow leaves very small. (See note E).
9	20 April	Larva started feeding.	Larva still a brown colour and not at all well camouflaged on young, green leaves. (See note F).
10	2 May	3rd skin change started.	
11	8 May	Skin change completed.	5 to 6 days normal for skin change. Larva now a bright green colour & well disguised.
12	24 May	4th skin change started.	
13	29 May	Skin change completed	Now in fifth & final instar. Appetite enormous & sallow leaves totally consumed. (See note G).
14	19 June	Ceased feeding & took up position under a leaf, with tail to stem and horns overlapping tip of leaf.	Leaf firmly fastened with silk to twig & a silk pad made on underside of leaf towards the stem.
15	24 June	No movement until this date, when pupation occurred.	For two days pupa remained almost horizontal.
16	26 June	Pupa hanging vertically.	It remained thus until eclosion. (See note H).
17	13 July	Imago ♂ emerged.	It was 19 days in the pupa state & had been a year, less 7 days, in my care. (See note J).

*This life is spent, preferably, in a muslin sleeve enclosing a portion of a bough on a Sallow bush, specially planted in your garden. Remember, the larva has to hibernate and this is best done 'au naturel' out of doors.

NOTES TO TABLE B

NOTE A

Almost invariably the female *iris* lays 2 eggs in a bush. Once, on 25/7/71, at Whiteparish, I found 2 ova on the same leaf. Both were fresh and, presumably, from the same female. If one egg is found, then a careful search must be made for a second. Remember that though the eggs may be laid quite close together on the bush, when the boughs are hooked down for examination the second egg may not turn up until quite a number of boughs have been searched.

One word of advice. By August, when the eggs are mostly laid, the sallow leaves often have small pimples on the upper surface. These galls are often about the same size and shape as an *iris* egg and can cause one's heart to leap unnecessarily. Practice will soon stop these false ecstasies!

As recorded elsewhere in this chapter a female can, at times, lay more than 2 eggs on a bush, so do not cease the search as soon as 2 eggs are found. Furthermore, several females may use the same bush. Over the years I have found that a bush, which appealed to a female in one year, will be equally attractive in subsequent years. Searching thus becomes easier the better the wood is known.

If the eggs are hatched in a box disaster will follow. When the young larva is put on a leaf in the sleeve it will wander and fail to settle. It will get on to the muslin and, when put back on a leaf, will wander again, until it dies of exhaustion. It would appear that it is searching for a position where the light is exactly suitable. The Greeks would undoubtedly have had a word for it; perhaps phototaxis is that word.

To stop this happening the leaf, with the egg upon it, must be pinned to a twig in the sleeve. It does not matter where, as long as the pin goes through the stem of the leaf.

The leaf will crumple or wither: no matter, the egg is securely stuck and in due time you will see the tiny, new born larva sitting on the tip of a leaf, head inwards. The egg shell will have disappeared — eaten by the larvae. The chosen leaf can be surprisingly far from the old, pinned leaf.

NOTE B

The larva in its second instar is an attractive little creature. It is exactly the same colour as the upper side of a sallow leaf and has a pair of horns, pink tipped, on the front end. Several pale yellow stripes slope diagonally backwards and upwards along its side; only the third stripe from the front reaches the top of the larva, where it meets its opposite number. This stripe is a deeper, brighter yellow than the others. The larva is covered in small, pale-gold warts, from which arise very short bristles. The effect of all this is to stop light being unduly reflected from the larva and so allows it to merge quite wonderfully into its background. Knowing that I had two larvae in a sleeve I have, nevertheless, had the greatest difficulty in finding them to show a visitor, only the frass in the sleeve convincing me they were still present.

On the subject of frass, it should be pointed out that it is distinctive; being long and cylindrical. Once, when watching quite a young larva, I saw it lift up its pointed tail to pass frass and then saw the larva bend its head round, seize the frass before it was dropped, and then throw it away with a flick of its head. In another chapter you will read how the young White Admiral larva decorates itself with frass. The seizing of frass by a young *iris* larva is, therefore, not without precedent.

NOTE C

This skin has to last from early September through to early May of the following year.

Although the larva eats all through October it grows very little, if at all. I believe that it is busy manufacturing 'anti-freeze'; because all through the winter it will lie completely exposed to ice, snow and bitter winds; but will suffer not at all from the severest weather.

NOTE D

The larva takes a few days wandering about before selecting its hibernaculum. This is normally in the fork formed by the junction of two twigs. It can, however, be on a twig, just below a leaf bud. Once, I had a larva which chose a dead leaf on which to hibernate. The leaf was firmly attached, with silk, to the twig. This had to be, because the *iris* larva (except in its first instar) never takes up a position on a leaf without attaching it to the twig. It is interesting to note that, whereas the majority of leaves within the sleeve fall to the bottom of the sleeve, those that have been used for food by the larvae, remain, brown and withered, on the twigs.

The hibernation pad is much thicker than the silken pad normally used by the larva, at the tip of a leaf, during its active life. Once the larva has settled on the hibernation pad, and become comatose, it is incapable of making a change and will die if disturbed. This, then, is one of the crisis points in the rearing of *iris*; because winter gales, and packed snow on the sleeve, may well dislodge the larva from its pad. I learnt the hard way that it is essential for the sleeve to be fitted with two wire hoops, each fixed to the branch enclosed by the sleeve. This will ensure the hibernating larva is not disturbed.

NOTE E

This is another crisis point. The hibernating larvae sometimes wake too soon, leave their pads, and take up a position beside a leaf bud (normal); but, this time, so early that they die of starvation before the sallow leaves are open. Fortunately, this does not often happen, but one year, 1972, I took some sallow and forced it indoors. As soon as leaves appeared I brought one of the two small larvae I had indoors and put it on this leafy sallow. It at once took up position at the tip of a leaf, spun a pad, and started eating. I thought all was well; but, on putting the larva back in the sleeve on a growing leaf, it developed ghastly diarrhoea and died. As its mate had died of starvation, I was 'irisless' for that year. I imagine this must sometimes happen in the wild and may well be one of the reasons for 'good' and 'bad' *iris* years.

NOTE F

This must be a critical time. The brown larva is not at all well camouflaged and the sooner the brown skin is changed for 'sallow-green' the better. However, this period lasts a fortnight or more.

NOTE G

This is the time when you may well have to put your sleeve on a fresh bough. Remember that the larva needs a nice, big leaf under which to pupate.

NOTE H

The procrypsis of the *iris* pupa is one of Nature's marvels. Whereas the larva was the bright green of the upper side of a sallow leaf, the pupa is the pale colour of the underside. Furthermore, it has veins exactly spaced to match those of the leaf's underside. Of course, one realises this is all due to natural selection over aeons of time. But still, let us marvel; let us rejoice that we have perception; even though that, in itself, may be due to natural selection!

I must explain that as soon as pupation is complete, and the pupa case hardened, I cut the leaf at the stem and bring it into my study. There I have an old-fashioned, 7 lb. biscuit-tin, which I call a 'pupatorium', suitably padded with cellulose wadding (*never* cotton-wool). On to the lid of this tin I fix, with 'Sellotape', the leaf by its stem. During the process the pupa sometimes protests in a most alarming way; it drums, most vehemently, on the tin-lid. At first I thought this must harm the pupa. But no — it is just a protective mechanism to frighten predators. Perhaps I am such a one. But if so a benign one; because, for many years, I have released every female *iris* I have bred. Thus, for one egg taken, I have put back, at the exact spot, at least 100 possible replacements. (I base this on the assumption that a female *iris* bears within her 100 eggs).

I vowed to myself that I would do this. If you break a promise made to yourself, then your promises made to other people must be pretty worthless. Indeed you are rubbish. So, often at considerable inconvenience, I have released my Empresses at the place where I found the egg.

I recount one such incident. A female *iris* had hatched in her biscuit tin in mid-July and, not being able to take her to her wood that day, I put her, overnight, in the 'fridge.

This makes butterflies comatose and so stops them flapping about and damaging themselves. Next morning I set off for her birth-wood. She was in a large pill-box and soon we arrived at the wood near Oxford. On arrival, I parked the car and peeped at the pill-box. All was well.

I entered the wood and walked up the main ride toward the sallow bush, where I had found the egg the previous year. On rounding a bend I saw about ten people standing exactly opposite the bush; in their midst was a man with 'WARDEN' inscribed on his armband. Most were gazing through binoculars at the top of the neighbouring oaks.

Somewhat non-plussed, I hesitated for a moment. Then, putting on my harmless old man act (considering my age, not very hard to do) I hobbled up to the group and enquired if they were looking for *iris*. They said they were. I remarked that I thought they were looking too high; to which the Warden replied 'Oh no, they live at the top of oak-trees'.

All this time I was surreptitiously removing the pill-box from my pocket. *Iris* had completely recovered from her chilblains and now crawled on to the top of my hand. I could feel her strong legs gripping my flesh. Suddenly I produced her. In the warmth of the sun she started, slowly, to open and close her wings. Being a female, there was no flash of purple, but her size and the beauty of the under-side markings were sufficient to make the spectators say 'Wow', or words to that effect. The wings began to move faster and the Warden called to a group of about four people, some hundred yards away, to come quickly. They ran to us and were just in time to see *iris* take her first flight. Slowly, and somewhat heavily, she flapped to the nearest oak. She did not make it to the top, but pitched on a leaf half-way up. There I left her, praying that a bird would not eat her before she mated and started laying. At least, I thought, she is high enough to escape human predation!

NOTE J

From my notes, over many years, it appears that the time from pupation to eclosion can be anything from 14 to 19 days. Females do not necessarily take longer to emerge than males.

I have rather contradictory data about whether females stay longer in the larval stage than males. On the whole, I would say that females actually do pupate later than the males and that the larva which produces a female is larger.

A BROWN STUDY

Over the flower-lit meadows of my youth a brown butterfly used to fly in swarms; it was the aptly named Meadow Brown, *Maniola jurtina*. In a warm spell, in late July, the whole meadow would appear to be on the move, as *jurtina*, with its weak, wavering flight fled before the walker. I do not suggest that *jurtina* is now a rare insect, far from it; but it no longer gives its impression of a locust-horde.

As a boy-collector I despised *jurtina*. It was common, and it was dull. My eyes were on the oak trees, bordering the meadows, hoping for a view of such beauties as the Purple Emperor or the Purple Hairstreak. How wrong I was. First, there is a sub-species known as *splendida*. It is very bright indeed and one has to go to the Western Isles, the Scilly Isles, Orkneys, Isle of Man, etc. to see it. Secondly, the variation in the distribution of spots on the underside of *jurtina's* hind-wings has led to a remarkable discovery by W.H. Dowdeswell, whom I knew when he was head of biology at Winchester College, and Kennedy McWhirter. Before coming to this I think it would help if I quoted from E.B. Ford*. 'It is a singular fact that some of the remarkable attributes of the commonest species may pass unobserved by generations of collectors. The Meadow Brown is one of the most familiar butterflies in England, yet it has not until lately been observed that the distribution of spotting on the underside of the hind-wings..... presents problems of unusual interest'. And McWhirter* 'Our knowledge of the processes of selection and the agents

* Moths by E.B. Ford p.215 (1955)
* Heredity Vol 22 Part 2 p.187 *et seq* (May 1967)

involved in them is still limited; it is not impossible that the spot distributions of distinct colonies are being maintained by a variety of selective agents operating at particular phases of the life-cycle of the insect'.

Now to the Dowdeswell-McWhirter discovery. Mr. Dowdeswell told me one day that they had found that a fungal infection occurred in the larvae of *jurtina*, and that the underside spotting of the *jurtina* imago was directly related to the ability of the larva to fight the infection. The reader must consult Dowdeswell's account fully to appreciate the matter, but, in short, the gene which gives a larva immunity to fungoid infection is also responsible for the imago's under-wing spotting. The previously held belief that the markings and patterns on the wings of a butterfly came solely through the forces of natural selection playing upon the imago does not apply to *jurtina*. One would probably be correct in supposing that it does not apply to other species as well.

Jurtina is a member of a family known as the *Satyridae*, and it is members of this family which make up this chapter. Countrymen call them 'The Browns'. Characteristic of this family are the varieties of spotting on the wings and these will be remarked upon as each species is considered. I selected *jurtina* to lead the dance because of her vulgarity, and because of the notoriety given her by Mr. Dowdeswell.

To follow her I choose the Mountain Ringlet, *Erebia epiphron**
— like going from the Pier at Southend to the exclusiveness of Balmoral. Well, not quite Balmoral; but not too far away. *Epiphron* is to be found over much of the Highlands at and above the 1500 ft. contour. In my experience it prefers rather flat areas, covered in a wiry grass. It is deep into this grass that the butterfly sinks as soon as the sun disappears and is then extremely difficult to find. It is a remarkable sight to see some dozen of the insect acting as one, as they vanish before one's eyes. It only takes one small cloud to do the trick!

Surprisingly, in England, it breeds considerably lower than is normal in Scotland. The usual rule for mountain species is 'the further South, the higher up'. Why this does not apply to

* One should add the subspecific titles of *mnemon* or *scotica*

33

epiphron I do not know, but I have seen the butterfly on Buttermere Fell at 1100 ft. and in the Wastwater area at 700 ft. This, surely, must be the lowest locality, worldwide, for *epiphron*.

While on this subject E.B. Ford, in his book 'Butterflies', says on page 288 'The Mountain Ringlet cannot live in England at an altitude of less than 1800 ft., but in Scotland it is able to descend to about 1500 ft.'. Ford's book is a wonderful contribution to our knowledge of British butterflies and, had he known the facts I give, he would doubtless have had some ideas to explain the anomaly.

As in *jurtina* the spotting on the undersurface of the hind-wings varies. Whether this is due to the 'Dowdeswellian factor' only research can show. Indeed, it would be remarkable if *jurtina* was the only butterfly to which this factor applied.

Epiphron is the smallest and the highest dwelling of Britain's three alpine butterflies. The other two are the Scotch Argus, *Erebia aethiops,* and the Large Heath, *Coenonympha tullia.* I turn now to *aethiops.* For a 'Brown' it is really quite a gaudy insect and, in sunlight, its bright, orange band across a deep, velvety-brown background makes a pretty sight. It is to be met with in Scotland and a few of its Isles; though there is still one locality in northern England where, in early August, I have seen it in great numbers. A lovely spot this, where the now so rare High-brown Fritillary still flies. This favoured spot, with its fine view of the distant high fells, also harbours a very small noctuid moth, which belies its Order by darting about in bright sunshine. So small and so swift is it, as to be caught only by those in their prime. For the rest, it is but a picture in a book!

Any variation in spotting occurs on the upperside — there are no spots on the underside of the hind-wing. The spotting on the upperside of the fore-wing consists, normally, of a double spot, a gap, and then a single spot. Occasionally there is a small dot in the gap. Another, fairly common, variation occurs in the colouration of the band on the underside of the hind-wing. This is, normally, blue-grey but occasionally is yellowish. This is the form called *ochracea* by Tutt. Its significance may well be Dowdeswellian.

So we come to the last of our alpines — the Large Heath,

Coenonympha tullia. No need to put on your mountain boots for this one; though do not hope to see it south of Borth in Wales or Whitchurch in Salop. To me *tullia* is the most interesting of the 'Browns'; in its *scotica* form it is also the most pleasing.

It is interesting because of its easily recognisable clines and the way in which they are geographically separated*. I set out, with a friend and his wife, to get the type form. This is generally agreed to be the one found on the peat bogs of Cumbria or North Lancashire and so, mid-morning on 3 July 1966, found us on a moss near Holkar in Cark-in-Cartmel. It was hot and sunny and *tullia* was in spate. In no time we had sufficient males and females for our purpose, which was to compare the type form with the rather spectacular cline to be found in Shropshire. In the pursuit of *tullia* we put up some interesting moths, the most beautiful being the tiny Purple-bordered Gold, *Idea muricata* which was in abundance. Some fifteen years later I took a keen moth-hunter friend to this delightful moss, only to find the whole place burned and not a Lepidoptera in sight. Farewell *tullia*!

At 14.30 hrs that afternoon we set off, with our booty, southward to Whitchurch, in the county of Shropshire. Here we booked in at a small hotel and, suitably washed and clad, we descended to the bar. You must realise that, at that time, I had no idea where the famous *tullia philoxenus* was to be found, save that it was somewhere near Whitchurch; so I asked, over a pint, a friendly-seeming local if there were any peat-diggings nearby. 'Why' he said 'the biggest peat-diggings in the County are just six miles down the road. I've even heard tell that they are the biggest in England. Its a place called Fenn's Moss'. He told me how to get there and for this I was most grateful. I asked if he knew who was the eponymous Mr. Fenn; but here the fountain stopped.

There is a pleasant, little moth on the British list called, in the vernacular, Fenn's Wainscot, *Photedes brevilinea* and, over supper, we considered the possibility that there might be some connection. Bernard Skinner, in his admirable book

* except in Ireland — see Ford's Butterflies p.292.

'Moths of the British Isles' states that it is 'A local species, confined to East Anglia'. Perhaps Mr. Fenn did not confine his mothing to his moss and occasionally visited the fens. Or perhaps he never caught a moth in his life and there was an East Anglian Fenn amongst the fens. This is getting a bit complicated and I leave it there.

Suitably refreshed we breakfasted, paid our bill, and stepped forth into a steady drizzle! No good hanging about in Whitchurch, so we set off for the moss. It was opening time when we arrived at the minor road leading to the moss and, providentially, there was a pub. If there was one thing more than *tullia* that appealed to my male friend, it was a pint of good ale. His wife was not too far behind. So we stayed and at 14.00 hrs the rain stopped, the sun came out and soon we were stumbling over the peat-hags of the moss. *Tullia philoxenus* warmed to the sun in numbers — in fact it was vulgarly common.

We left the hags at 15.30 hrs and arrived at my friend's home, near Beaconsfield, at 20.00 hrs.

So finished a typical butterfly foray — taking one into unspoilt terrain, after esoteric quarry in pleasant company. Why be greedy and ask for more?

In recent years Fenn's moss, and the adjacent Whixall moss, have hit the headlines. Continuous peat extraction has not done a remarkable area any good. This is a pretty big area; one looks across its flat, rather black face, to the horizon and will not readily find its like in mid-England. The appropriate Ministry has sat up and taken notice; there is talk of stopping peat extraction. In the meantime, *philoxenus* still flies there, and the Northern Footman, *Eilema sericea,* can be attracted to light in suitable places. I put a light there on the night of 30 July 1990 and was delighted to see seven of this striking moth on the sheet before mid-night. These two Shropshire mosses are the headquarters of this insect in Britain, outside of which the insect is unknown.

To return to *tullia.* Having set my few examples from Cark and from Shropshire, I was able to examine them in detail. The difference was striking, chiefly on the underside. On the upperside Shropshire *tullia* was darker, one male specimen being of a chocolate colour. On the underside, the 'eye-spots' were twice as big on *philoxenus* as on the Cark type, and the upper spot on the fore-wing often had a small 'satellite'. To sum up — *philoxenus* is a darker, more vividly spotted insect.

Seeing how the *tullia* clines could vary, I was more than ever determined to see what *tullia scotica* looked like. The chance came on a mothing trip to Skye. I was there in search of a Burnet subspecies, *Zygaena lonicerae jocelynae* (Trem)*. This moth is confined to a few coastal areas on the Isle of Skye and is the sort of sub-species collectors like to see — no messing, it is really different.

In pursuit of this nice bug, one sunny morning, the 1st of July, found me motoring down Glen Brittle and gazing up at the splendid Cuillin Hills. There, on the moors below Squr Thullon (2885 ft.), I saw *tullia scotia* wavering over the heather. It was just emerged and in all its elegant finery. It is rather a hairy butterfly and, when really fresh, these fine hairs show up as a lovely pale blue on the underside. The pale, soft brown of the upperside and the grey-blue of the underside of the hindwings, unmarked by spotting, give an overall impression of soft elegance. When I show my short series to people, who often know little about butterflies, they never fail to comment on its beauty. You do not have to have garish colouring to be well-dressed!

At the time I had not read Ford's 'Butterflies' and so did not know that Wales had another, though unnamed, cline to offer. As it was, my friend, General Lipscomb, told me to go to Lake Bala, in Wales, and search for the Welsh *tullia*. Accordingly, on 1st July 1967, I took one of my young sons to Lake Bala to help in the search. He was a keen fisherman, and a promise of an evening's fishing on the lake was sufficient bribe to get him to help me find an obscure brown butterfly, in which he, and his brothers, had no possible interest. Our search round Lake Bala was haphazard and unsuccessful. The weather did not help. This same weather was, however,

---

* This sub-species was discovered on Skye in June 1961. It is found nowhere else in the British Isles. Its finder was R.F. Bretherton and he named it Jocelynae after his wife, who, I believe, actually saw it first.

conducive to good fishing and, in the evening, we put up our rods and each caught one trout, of about 1 lb., on a Welsh favourite, the Coch-y-bondhu. So we had grilled trout for supper and time to think. I recalled having once seen a fine, peaty-looking bog on a journey from Machynlleth to Aberystwyth. Surely, I thought, if *tullia* is a Welshman he will live on Borth Bog. So, early on 2nd July, we set off south to Borth via Machynlleth. I can never pass through Machynlleth without recalling the story of the girl, who got what is euphemistically called into 'trouble'. She went, tearfully, to her father for help. He was most upset and said she must 'get it seen to'. He pointed out that his position in the community was such that no scandal must occur and that she would have to go to London.

'But who', said the girl 'can I see in London?'

'There is a famous Welsh doctor in London, Dr. Vaughan Williams. Go to him, tell him you are a Welsh girl, and he will look after you'.

'How do I find him?' asked the girl.

'Just look him up in the telephone book' replied her Dad.

So to London went the girl and duly turned up at a fine, big house in a handsome square. She rang the bell and the polished mahogany door was opened by a large butler.

'Can I see the Doctor, please' said the girl.

'I am very sorry' the butler said 'but he's very busy just now orchestrating the "Men of Harlech".'

'Well', said the girl, 'when you next see him, perhaps you could ask him to orchestrate the men of Machynlleth as well.'

This time it was sunny, Butterfly weather, and I drove slowly along the minor road to Borth. The bog was on our left and I stopped at the entrance to a cart-track leading into it. My son, who had long hoped to give my net a whirl, leaped out of the car, ran down the track, jumped the ditch beside it and was amongst the heather. Soon I saw him running and striking with the net. Time and again he struck. I only hoped it was *tullia* he was after. No need to worry; — he was soon back with his haversack full of pill-boxes and the pill-boxes contained *tullia*. I went through them carefully, releasing worn specimens, and was left with a short series of what faintly resembled *tullia scotica.* They were paler than the Cark specimens, though not as pale as *scotica,* and with spotting so small as, at times, closely to resemble a vestigially spotted *scotica.*

In studying the maps in Ford's 'Butterflies' I see that subspecies *'scotica'* is shown as being the one flying at Borth. So Wales has been robbed of *'tullia cymru'*! I agree that the insects we caught at Borth that day most closely resemble *scotica;* but they are but a dull edition of the beautiful *tullia* of Glen Brittle.

Enough of *tullia.* It is now the turn of Britain's commonest butterfly to take the stage. I refer to the Small Heath, *Coenonympha pamphilus.* And common it is. No matter where you go, from May to September, you are likely to see this slow flying, little, brown butterfly. The main point of interest seems to be in finding out how it continues to remain on the wing for so long a period. South, in 'Butterflies of the British Isles', considers it is due to the partial emergence of some broods and consequent delayed emergences. He is well worth reading on this matter.

As far as I am concerned, I can only recall one point of interest. When collecting in Glen Brittle, Isle of Skye, I caught a gigantic female of this species. So big that she was masquerading as *tullia* and had me fooled. I do not know if the *pamphilus* of the Scottish Isles are normally given to such hugeness — perhaps the grasses of Glen Brittle contain some special nutritive; or is this normal for the Hebrides?

Now to a favourite of mine — the Ringlet, *Aphantopus hyperantus.* This velvety, almost black, butterfly takes a walk on the shady side — in other words, it flits slowly and waveringly along the edges of woods, or along woodland rides, out of direct sun-light. Like all the Browns, it has ocellated spots. These occur on all the wings, but are much more pronounced on the underside. They vary in number, but not so markedly as in *jurtina.* It is the variability in size and shape of the spots that makes *hyperantus* of interest. At the annual exhibition of the British Entomological and Natural History Society there are usually one or two remarkable varieties of this butterfly to be seen, ranging from var *obsoleta* to var *lanceolata.*

E.B. Ford, in his 'Butterflies', considers the genetics of

these vars. He believes that the reduction of spots is controlled on a multi-factorial basis*, while *lanceolata* is inherited as a simple recession. Whatever the scientific findings may be, it is well worth giving close attention to the many Ringlets one will see during a woodland walk in July. Suddenly, as happened to me one day in a Hampshire wood, one may see a really striking var. Mine was a female and on the underside of the left fore-wing the top spot had exploded! The spots normally consist of a white-centred black pupil, surrounded by a narrow, cream-coloured ring. In this case the cream ring had become a large, circular patch.

Before leaving *Hyperantus* it might be worth giving a thought to its scientific name. It was so meaningless that people decided Linnaeus had meant it to be called Hyperanthus or even Hyperanthes (a son of Darius). It was *Hyperanthus* in a book of labels I bought many years ago.

Thus it appears as *Hyperanthus* in my collection. Now it is officially back to what Linnaeus named it. Old Linnaeus called species some wonderful names. Consider his name for a common British bird — the Wheatear. He dubbed it *Oenanthe*. This means, in Greek, 'The flower of the vine' or, perhaps, 'Bloom on the grapes'. Aristotle, in his Historia Animalium, 633 A15, called a bird, possibly a Wheatear, by this name*; though how the Wheatear fits I can not see.

The English vernacular name is more easily explained. Some shepherd of long ago, tending his sheep on, say, the South Downs, noticed this newly arrived spring migrant and, further, remarked on its alarm note. This clearly said 'Wheat-Ear'. There are those who dispute this, saying that the shepherd noticed its white rump and said to himself 'Ah, there be that old "White Arse" again — 'e be earlier than ever this year and 'is arse be even whiter'.

We now leave the shady, woodland rides and venture into sunlit lanes and open downland in search of the Gatekeeper,

---

* see also under *jurtina* and McWhirter's views
* I am grateful to Mrs. Helen Brock of Oxford for this esoteric information.

Pyronia tithonus. This butterfly has had many vernacular names — Speckled Wall, Wall Butterfly (vide Rev. F.O. Morris 1893); Small Meadow Brown, Hedge Brown, Large Heath (vide South 1921) and The Hedge Eye (Petiver 1717)*. Gatekeeper, however, seems to suit it best. A break in the hedge, caused by a gate, is where the sun shines the brightest and that is where this insect is happiest. This is where it stakes a territory and is the place to which it returns, time and again, when disturbed. Despite the aptness of its English name, I have found it in great numbers amongst the Juniper bushes on the Hampshire Downs. Shake a Juniper bush on a hot day in mid July and *tithonus* flops out in amazing numbers. This enables one to examine many individuals and so I have done. Many, many individuals and no startling finds. This appears to be one of the most stable of the Browns. I think this question of stability is worth a moment's pause.

In the 1950's I spent a lot of time during their breeding season studying Cirl Buntings, *Emberiza cirlus* and Yellow Hammers, *Emberiza citronella.* Both were plentiful at that time in parts of Sussex and Hampshire. They frequently nested quite close to each other and in similar sites. It would appear that if selective factors had any bearing on egg-colouration in these two species, then they would apply equally to both. Such is not the case. The eggs of the Cirl Bunting show remarkable homogeneity; those of the Yellow Hammer quite the reverse, with ground colour varying from pink, through brown to pure white. There is nothing geographical in all this; the eggs of the two species remain the same throughout their breeding range. The idea occurs that the Cirl Bunting is a very old species and that the genes which produce egg variation have long been eliminated; experimentation is finished. Not so with the Yellow Hammer; variation in egg colouration is remarkable. It is a newer species and still awaits selective forces to make a decision. All this is surmise, but perhaps it may apply throughout Nature. In which case, I would suggest,

---

* Petiver was very fond of using the term 'eye'. He had many 'eyes' — and they will be referred to in due course.

41

tithonus is an early butterfly species. My knowledge of *tithonus* is largely based on Hampshire specimens. It could well be that elsewhere in Britain there occurs more variety.

The Speckled Wood, *Pararge aegeria*, used to go by such attractive names as Wood Lady or Wood Argus*. Especially appealing to butterfly lovers as just about the first butterfly to be seen in the woodland year; appearing in late March in favourable Springs and continuing through the year to September*.

This long emergence is due to the fact that the Speckled Wood can pass the Winter either as a pupa or as a larva. It is the only British butterfly to do this and it produces interesting colour variation. The first generation thus emerges over a long period (late March to May), with subsequent extended emergence of the second brood. In fact, there is an overlap in the generations and it is of interest to note a quick method of identification. In Gen I the pale, whitish markings surrounding the 'eye' on the fore-wing, extend well beyond the 'eye' towards the rim. In Gen II these markings do not extend beyond the 'eye'. It has always seemed to me that the Gen I specimens are both larger and more ornate than later emergencies and, from a decorative aspect, carry the Wood Lady to the top of the Browns!

Throughout its long emergence this butterfly behaves in the same way. It flits, in dappled shade, about the woodland paths, returning to the same leaf again and again after sparring with a neighbour. These fluttering fights are harmless affairs. The two insects mount upwards as they battle together and, when in mid-foliage of the trees, separate and glide down to their respective leaves beside the path. Like most things in life there is, doubtless, some sexual significance.

I can not leave the Speckled Wood without recording that on 5th May 1958, in the New Forest, Hampshire, I was lucky enough to see and capture a ♀ specimen like the nominate,

* see Rev. E.O. Morris.
* The odd Brimstone, *Goneptoryx cleopatra*, of course, can appear in February from hibernation.

42

which is normal in Southern Europe. This is a very rare UK variety.

I continue with genus *Lasiommata*. Our only member of this genus is the Wall Butterfly (*megera*). I have little to say about it except that, unlike the Speckled Wood, the males carry a sex mark on the fore-wings. Also, unlike its cousins, it relishes the full glare of the sun. The Wall has a patchy distribution in Britain and in many areas it is never seen. If it is found in your neighbourhood make a point of catching one and, with your pocket magnifying glass, study the underside of the hind-wings. There you will see some of the most intricate, delicate and altogether exquisite markings to be seen on an insect. You may well, like me, wonder to what end all this labour is designed coming, as it does, from a green gunge, which was the contents of a pupa but a few weeks before.

We are coming nearly to the end of our Brown study. Wrapped in thought we wonder how it comes that there are seventeen species of butterfly in Europe carrying the vernacular name of Grayling. The British contribute just one — The Grayling, *Hipparchia semele*. There must be something very conducive to survival in the general appearance of these Grayling, for they all look very alike. They thrive all over Europe, mostly on moorlands or rough waste places, but occasionally in thinly wooded areas from sea level to 1800 m. Sometimes it is only by study of the genitalia that the species can be separated.

The Grayling, in Britain, shows remarkable variety both in size and in the colour of the underside. I have specimens from the Chalk Downs round Winchester with very pale undersides and others from Skye with the underside almost black. I have specimens from Cornwall with females as big as a Red Admiral, *Vanessa atalanta;* and some males from the New Forest no bigger than a Meadow Brown, *jurtina*. There is a pygmy race on the Great Orme, in North Wales, of wondrous smallness. There must be something special about the Great Orme, because it also produces a pygmy race of the Silver Studded Blue, *Plebejus argus*.

I suspect it may be true of all the species of Grayling, but I have no first hand knowledge of it abroad. I refer to the habit of our *semele* of at once, on landing, aligning itself with the sun so that no shadow is thrown. The Greeks doubtless had a word for it. It is remarkable to watch. As the insect lands on the ground it at once closes its wings and shuffles round so that they are aligned with the sun. If it means leaning the whole body over, then this is done. There the butterfly remains rigid and is extremely difficult to see. If you should ever find yourself en-famille in the New Forest on a sunny day in mid-July then, instead of allowing the children to feed the ponies, which is not only forbidden but also stupid, let them roam the heath until they flush a 'Rock-eyed Underwing' (Petiver's name for *semele*) and, hastening after it, watch it settle. If it doesn't do what I have said then give them a quid, or an ecu, or whatever. Your money will be safe.

Just to be awkward, I have left the Marbled White, *Melanargia galathea,* to the end. In scientific works the Half-Mourner or Marmoress (vide Morris) is at the head of the Satyridae — the Browns. But as most people look on it as a 'White' I felt it made an unsuitable beginning for what has been a 'Brown study'. Be that as it may, *galathea* is lovely in her own right and a suitable finale to a mostly sombre lot of bugs.

She flies in the close company of her mates and so, where one is seen, others will quickly follow. I associate this butterfly with hot days on the downs and have always kept an eager look out for varieties. Such range from pure, creamy white to completely black. I have but once seen a variety and it was the real thing. I was hunting Cotley Hill, in Wiltshire, for the beautiful, but rare, Scarce Forester, *Adscita globulariae,* when I saw an almost totally black Marbled White flying down the hill towards the footpath at the bottom. With my net at the ready I sped in pursuit. I had a certain amount to catch up and the steep slope did not help me. As I neared the footpath I saw there was a barbed-wire fence separating it from a cornfield. The butterfly flew over the fence and sped on over the standing corn. I was seriously held up in getting through the wire and when I stood up amongst the corn I could no longer see my quarry. I gazed into the distance for a long time, but never saw my Full Mourner again.

That evening I rang up my friend, General Lipscomb, who

lived not far from Cotley Hill, and told him of my sighting. He was most interested. He later told me he had spent the better part of two days waiting and watching on Cotley Hill and on the hills the far side of the cornfield. To no avail. I reminded him that our grandfathers called it the 'Half-mourner', so he should be prepared for a little sorrow!

Lippy had, I believe, the finest collection of butterfly vars in private hands at that time. I had often taunted him with his amazing luck. He used to smile and say luck was directly proportional to time spent in the field. I now knew what he meant. His collection was bequeathed to the British Museum (Nat. Hist); but he got a most talented painter of butterflies, A.D.A. Russwurm, to paint his vars. These, enclosed in vellum, remain in the hands of his family and are a fitting memorial to a most perceptive collector.

PUTTING ON THE RITZ

This means dressing up in top-hat and tails and then dancing like Fred Astaire. My butterfly has no top hat, but it does have tails and it dances most elegantly — it is the Swallow Tail, *Papilio machaon*. To be precise, it is of the British race, *britannicus*, that I write. This differs in three respects from its nearest Continental neighbour, *gorganus*, found in France. Its habitat is different, being confined to Fens and Broads; its larval pabulum is different, consisting of Milk Parsley, *Peucedanum palustre* and its markings are heavier, with a darker yellow background. E.B. Ford considers it arrived in Britain in the 3rd Pleistocene Interglacial Period.

I had often seen *machaon* in Germany and France, and had seen magnificent members of the *papilio* genus in the foothills of the Himalayas; but, from boy-hood, I had longed to see our native Swallowtail. So once again I teamed-up with Dr. Jim Whitby; this time for a trip to the Broads.

We arrived at Hickling Staithe Guest House at 19.30 hours on 29 May 1959. At 10.00 hours the next morning we got out of the car and stepped on to the famous Catfield Common. There was no sun, but it was warm. At 11.00 hours the sun broke through momentarily and we became alert. At 11.10 hours I saw my first British *machaon* and caught same — a perfect ♂. In the next half-hour we caught 4 *machaon* out of 6 seen. All were worn and released. At 12.00 hours we decided to try our luck elsewhere, and moved to Sutton Broad. As we got to the end of the road at Longmoor Point, Jim got out of the car and said 'This is no damn good'. (And, indeed, it did not look very good — a field, with cows, on one hand, and a large, private garden on the other).

At that instant a *machaon* flopped over the bonnet of the car, over the wire fence and into the field. Jim acted with commendable despatch. He seized a net from the back of the car, leaped the wire fence and caught *macheon* as he danced among the cows. You will note that I refer to *machaon* as 'he'. I do this because Machaon was Chief Medical Officer attached to the Greek Expeditionary Force (under command of General Agamemnon) to Troy. In modern parlance, I suppose Comd Med would have been his title. I do not know what wag decided to choose the name of a RAMC Colonel as suitable for the scientific name of this fine butterfly. Whereas the authors of books on birds, moths and many other orders give the name of the name-giver (eg Hubner, Hufnagel, Freyer, Tutt etc.), few do this for Butterflies.

Neither South nor Ford do, though Morris does, in a quaint way: he gives 8 names for the inventor of *machaon* as a scientific name for the Swallow-Tail — you pays your money and you takes your choice! Linnaeus is my pick, because Higgens & Riley, authors of Butterflies of Britain & Europe (1970), not only give the authority for scientific names, but also the date. In the case of *P. machaon* they give Linnaeus 1758. I do not suggest that this great man was a wag. I do suggest that he had some quaint advisers.

This digression has given time for my friend, Jim, to return to the car with his trophy and to recover his breath. At that moment a keeper, a Mr. Starling, came out of the drive-gate and said we were trespassing. We did not deny this. He said we must come up to the big house and see the owner — Mr. Whitlock. So we were marched up the drive, through a lovely garden, to meet the owner in front of his fine house. He was interested in our venture and most kind. As we stood talking, we saw *machaon* everywhere; some on Lilac and no less than three on one bloom of Lupin. We had no nets! Mr. Whitlock told us to fetch them and we took one perfect specimen each off the Lilac bush near the front door. To see Britain's largest butterfly, gleaming in the sun, in such charming surroundings and in such numbers, was full recompense for being arrested by a chap called Starling. Indeed, over 30 years on, I bless his name; until he starts building a nest in my roof.

With the owner's permission we were now free to roam Sutton Broad. We walked down a lane into the heart of the Broad and were greeted by the boom of a Bittern. It was so close that we could hear the intake of breath before the bump. Country folk, in these parts, used to call the bird the 'Bitter Bump' which, unlike *machaon*, has decreased alarmingly. Suitably thrilled by this experience we left the track and entered a reedy and very rough bit of broadland. *Machaon* was flying everywhere; but impossible to catch. So we flattened a narrow strip of reeds, for about 60 yards, and placed ourselves, rather like tennis players at the net, ready to intercept *machaon* as he or she flew over the reeds. They were all coming the same way, downwind, and we would shout to one another 'Your bird'. Unfortunately, *machaon* does not stay for long on one course and almost invariably we would meet on the same target. This often led to a frightened *machaon* escaping. *Machaon*'s normal flight is slow and wavering; when frightened he's up and away — fast. We caught over 20 butterflies; but released them all. It is an insect very liable to damage and amongst the tall reeds is especially prone. We learnt a lot about *machaon*, however, and saw several pairs 'in cop'. In our catch, the sexes were about equal. This day, 30 May, we had 3 hours sunshine. We had caught a lot of *machaon* and could have caught more; but, in fact, we had retained only 2 each — perfect specimens.

Next day, 31 May, we decided to revisit Catfield Common and search for ova. On our first visit to this Common, Jim reckoned he had seen a female *machaon* laying eggs on a patch of marshy ground the other side of a small river. I had brought my blow-up dinghy (ex. R.A.F. surplus stores) for just such an eventuality. It carried only one person, so Jim got aboard and soon disembarked on the far bank. As I watched him, I thought of the many times I and friends had used this in Scotland. I thought, particularly, of the time I had used it to reach a small island far out in a loch in Wester Ross. I had wished to see the nest and eggs of the Black-throated Diver, *Colymbus articus*, and, through glasses, I had seen the diver scramble ashore. I was rewarded for my long paddle by the sight of the two, long, brown eggs in a scrape at the end of a

Swallowtail

3 ft. path made by the bird, as it struggled on its breast from the water's-edge. A day later my friend and I were having a drink in an Inn not far from this loch, where we heard two ghillies talking together. One said 'No — the boats had not been used'. (It was a fishing loch). The other said 'Then he must have swum'. The first replied 'Then he must have been a fine swimmer — there were boot marks where he landed'. We left them, shaking their heads.

I returned to the car to await Jim's return, when I saw a large, female *machaon* flopping low over the Common and occasionally pitching. To my joy, I realised she was ovipositing. I followed her and collected a dozen eggs from the leaves of the Milk Parsley. At this date the plant was not more than a foot high and the eggs were easy to spot. They were pale green in colour and not much smaller than the eggs of a Poplar Hawk, *Laothoe populi*. Jim returned from his water-borne expedition with 18 ova, found by cold-searching. The weather was very hot, but not much sun. For the record, we had 3 hours of sun on the 30th and 1 hours on the 31st. This was sufficient for us to see a wonderful flight of *machaon*. We reckoned we saw 150 plus during the day and a half we were in the area, with males and females about equal. The female is considerably larger than the male and paler.

I arrived home in Hampshire confident that all would go well with the ova. My wife was very keen on her herb-garden and always grew some fennel, *Faeniculum vulgare*. This year there was a particularly robust clump, which I enclosed with muslin, tied to four long canes. The edges of the muslin I buried in the earth. The first eggs hatched on 12 June, having by this time turned a purplish-black colour. It would appear that *machaon* eggs take 12 days to hatch — though, as my eggs were kept indoors, this may not be entirely accurate. The newly hatched larvae, having been given time to eat their egg-shells, were soon munching fennel. They were black, with a white saddle-mark, and looked uncommonly like a bird-dropping. This disguise is used by quite a lot of insects in their various stages — some as larvae; some as pupae; (I am thinking particularly of the pupa made by some Brachonid members of Hymenoptera, which are parasites) and some as imagos. Nature is full of cunning plans; she knows no-one wants to eat bird-droppings. And so did Darwin!

I kept a record of skin changes, as follows:

1st moult after 9 days	(still black and white)
2nd moult after 15 days	(now gingerish)
3rd moult after 20 days	(now green and orange and black)
Girdled up on 27th day	(Larva assumes an upright position against stem and ties itself to stem, by a girdle)
Pupated on 30th day	
Imago, a male, emerged on 47th day	(17 days passed as a pupa)

Thus, typically, *machaon* spends 12 days as an egg; 30 days as a larva and 17 days as a pupa. This gives a total of 59 days from new-laid egg to imago. I believe the female spends 19 days as a pupa and so emerges two days later than a male. All this applies only to the late July-early August emergences. The October pupae have to over-winter on their reed stems.

It gave me great pleasure watching my *machaon* larvae grow. Especially, in their fourth instar, they were spectacular. They now had what is called the osmeterium. This is a v-shaped, orange-coloured, apparatus kept hidden in a fold behind the head. When alarmed, it is protruded. It is said to give out an unpleasant smell, but I can not say I ever smelt it. Actually, I very seldom saw it protruded. So many people came to see the larvae in their fennel compound that they became tame and were seldom alarmed. They made, indeed, a splendid sight in a Hampshire garden. I was tempted to release some of the imago, but then recollected what happened to Spedan Lewis's experiment in his large estate on the Test at Leckford and Longstock. It happened before I came to live at Leckford, but I learned about it from him. Not long after World War II he acquired some hundreds of *machaon* eggs and released the subsequent larvae in the large reed beds that flank the Test in those parts. In due course *machaon* emerged in all his tailed glory and Spedan had great hopes of a successful introduction. The insects, however, spread far and wide and none appeared the next year. Local gossip has it that one flew across the road just in front of the local Postman, who promptly fell off his bike. As he picked himself up he was heard to mutter 'I'll never touch the stuff again'. But the Post got through as I am through with *machaon*.

BIRTH OF THE BLUES

According to E.B. Ford (and who better to follow?) the Blues are of the Family Lycaenidae; sub-family Lycaenicae; tribe Polyommatini. I start with the Silver Studded Blue, *Plebejus argus L.,* though there is no reason why this should be promoted Tribal Leader as far as I know. The eggs, which over winter, are commonly laid on gorse and it therefore follows that gorse is frequently present in its habitats. Thus the sandy heaths of the New Forest, sprinkled over with gorse, are *the* place to see this insect. Go in July. There are other food-plants, and this probably accounts for the presence of this Blue in sites very different to those of the Hampshire and Surrey heaths.

Wherever sandy heath with gorse patches occurs, there *P. argus* is likely to be found. Unfortunately, the greedy builders have their eyes on just such waste land. Compromises can be found, as shown by one enterprising and conservation-minded Norfolk Council. In this case great hunks of the heath were transplanted in another area and so *P. argus* was saved. I remember reading in the Press at the time 'Rare butterfly saved'. Of course, this butterfly is by no means rare, but it makes a good headline. How many times does one find an article in the Press, on a subject about which one knows a little, to contain falseness. Not long ago in the 'Field', of all magazines, I saw a picture of a Wren, *T. t. troglodytes,* feeding young in the nest. This bird builds a domed nest, with a side entrance. The picture had been printed 90° wrong, so that the nest was shown as a normal open-topped nest. One wonders how much that is written in the Press on subjects, about which one knows nothing, equally contains tripe!

P. argus does not provide the exciting vars found in some others of the tribe; but it does produce two very distinctive sub-species. First to sub-species *caernensis* Thompson. The larvae feed on Rock Rose, *Helianthemum,* and, as the Latin name of the sub-species indicates, it flies, mainly, in North Wales. On 12 July 1981 I went to a gigantic lump of limestone known as the Great Orme on the North Wales coast. First, who was Mr. Orme and why he was great I don't know. To be factual, I believe its full name is Great Orme's Head. So he had a great head! I was there with a friend in search of a rare moth — the Silky Wave, *Idaea dilutaria.* We paid our 30p. toll and went anti-clockwise up and round the Head.

It is a pleasant ride with, at times, precipitous views of the sea below. As one nears the end of the circuit, and comes away from the sea, a large area of waste land appears. We parked in a layby and began tapping through the scrub, hoping to flush the Silky Wave. In this we were unsuccessful but, at once, realised we were among a strong colony of small, blue butterflies. On catching some, we were delighted to see *caernensis,* both male and female. They were much smaller than the normal *P. argus;* had hardly any black border to the wings; had no orange lunules on the upper side and the females were blue instead of brown. Altogether a sub-species of note!

They had obviously been on the wing for some time and only a very few were collectable. However, I had enough to show *caernensis* to be a beautiful little butterfly in its own right.

In a desultory way, with no success, I have searched the mosses round Witherslack in Cumbria for the other *P. argus* sub-species — *masseyi.* I often wonder who was the lucky Mr. Massey, who chanced upon this butterfly. Quite a few moths have been called after their discoverers. Captains Blomer and Mathews, Messrs. Fenn, Ashworth, Haworth, Dumeril, Eversmann, Freyer, Porter, Weaver and, of course, the industrious Dr. Blair to name a few. But our British butterflies are not so eponymously inclined. Albin has his Eye, to match that of Mr. Petiver, and Weaver has his Fritillary. I wish I knew more about some of these people — what, for instance, did Captain Blomer say when he first saw his Rivulet — perhaps it included the word 'Egad'.

To return to *masseyi*. I can find no evidence of its present existence. Its domain was the mosses on the borders of Lancashire and Westmorland with the main concentration at Witherslack. It was larger than *caernensis* and, like that sub-species, the female was blue. The underside was unusually pale. Ford, writing in 1945, thought the insect was recovering, after having been nearly extinct; but this recovery, if, indeed, it ever occurred, was short lived. Of interest is that, at a meeting of the British Entomological and Natural History Society (the modern name of the old 'South London') on 23 September 1971, Mr. P.N. Crow stated that *masseyi* was present in Westmorland until 1926, when a severe frost at the end of May wiped out the insect. This statement was not challenged at the time. I have carefully searched through all subsequent issues of the Bulletin of this Society and there has been no further reference to *masseyi*.

There are those who say that *masseyi* was over-collected and that its loss is due to this. They could well be right. In my opinion careful collecting has done no harm to any lepidopteral species. However, the butterfly under review and the New Forest Burnet, *Zygaena viciae*,* a moth, were grossly over-collected and this probably was the main cause of their disappearance.

I can not leave the Orme without recording that a single Silky Wave visited my M.V. light that night and so my cup was full — of my favourite Malt.

Next, padded-up and waiting to come in, is Sir Garfield Sobers? No — its the Brown Argus. Much the same, being the right colour with a marvellous eye! I have, of course, honoured this pleasant little butterfly by mentioning it in the same breath as probably the greatest all-rounder ever to grace a cricket field; but it needs a bit of a boost. *Aricia agestis* is a small, brown butterfly without a trace of blue. The wings, on the upperside, are faintly bordered with orange lunules. On the underside it is profusely dotted with black-centred white eyelets, hence the name 'Argus'. So much for *agestis* in its

* *Z. v. argyllensis* Tremewan has since been discovered in Scotland in 1963.

normal, southern form found chiefly on chalky or sandy soil. As the species proceeds northwards in Britain, subtle changes take place in the markings. In the past this led to much erroneous classification, which E.B. Ford does his best to sort out. But even he is not too easy to follow. For instance, on one page he refers to sub-species and then calls them races. Previously he uses the term 'clines' or hybrid populations. One of his sub-species, *Aricia artaxerxes,* has now been given full specific status, under the name Mountain Argus. It is found in Scotland, the mountains of Scandinavia, the Alps, Pyrennes etc. and even in the Atlas mountains of North Africa.

So the famous Castle Eden Dene Argus is a hybrid, a mongrel. Note that it is not a mule or it would not have bred. I find it difficult, still, fully to understand all this. If *artaxerxes* and *agestis* are truly separate species then any mating between them would produce mules not mongrels. I have never searched for the Castle Eden Dene Argus (known, at one time, as var *salmacis* Stephens) but I took this cutting from the Daily Telegraph, dated 11 April 1981 — 'A rare butterfly species, the Castle Eden Argos (sic), could be threatened if plans to extend a quarry went ahead, an enquiry was told yesterday. Nature Conservancy Council representatives said that the butterfly, found only in Co. Durham, would be in danger if a dolomite quarry at Thrislington was enlarged by 100 acres'.

You will note that it is here called a species — not a sub-species, not a 'var', not a hybrid nor a cline. Some years ago I had occasion to visit a famous lawyer, Sir David Napley, for his advice on certain aspects of a Wild Life Protection Act. It was a remarkable experience. I first told him my problem. He then, quick as a bird, skipped from book to book on his massive shelves; asking me questions as he sped and then making a remark, which I have never forgotten; 'This is full of law'. Finally, he called in his short-hand secretary and, without notes, he dictated to her his views, occasionally glancing at me for approval as to facts. The lady left and we discussed some aspects of the matter. Shortly, she returned and I read a couple of pages of the clearest, neatest advice possible. The nettles and brambles had vanished and the way ahead was clear. Wonderful! I am sure Sir David would solve the 'Mystery at Castle Eden Dene' just as quickly as Holmes solved his problems. *Salmacis* is now regarded as a subspecies of *A. artaxerxes.*

I have enjoyed hunting *artaxerxes* in his Highland haunts. I have seen him, in plenty, on banks beside the A9 in the Killiecrankie area and in glades beside the north shore of L. Rannoch. In fact, wherever the rock-rose, *Helianthemum chamaecistus,* grows in the Highlands, there, I would say, *artaxerxes* will flourish. He or she is immediately recognisable by the pure, white discal spot on the upperside of the forewings and by the fact that, on the underside, the white eyelets have no black centres. How natural selection comes into all this some bright, young scientist of the future will discover.

Now we come to the big one — the Large Blue, *Maculinea arion.* There are people who say this butterfly is still to be found in the British Isles (excluding the carefully guarded areas where the insect has been introduced from abroad); but I, personally, doubt this very much. I consider it to be a lost British species and, as such, I suppose it rightly has no place in this book. However, its loss has been so recent and I have such vivid memories of seeing it flying in numbers in a north Cornish coomb that its inclusion here seems appropriate.

The first thing to realise is that *arion* is a very specialised species and, as such, is vulnerable. Nature has produced many such 'specialists' amongst the various faunal and floral Orders; many of remarkable deviousness. Consider the Huia, *Heteralocha acutirostris,* a bird that used to inhabit New Zealand. Here the cock had a short, powerful bill and the hen a long, slender curved one. Their main diet was a grub that lives at the end of a long tunnel in the stem of a tree. The cock's task was to break open the tunnel; the hen could then extract the grub. A splendid arrangement, except for the fact that, alone, the sexes died of starvation. A wonderful deterrent to divorce! It meant, however, that the species was always very vulnerable and thus liable to extinction. How natural selection achieves such marvels is not easily explainable. Perhaps the following extract from a letter by Darwin* may hold a clue:

* P462 of 'Darwin' by Desmond & Moore.

'Organic beings are not perfect, only perfect enough to struggle with their competitors...new adaptations could not be perfect, as the old theologians had taught, or there would be no competition, no selection, and no progress. Imperfection was nature's rule.'

What one can extract from this is that specialisation can lead to perfection and so, breaking nature's rule, has to be removed.

Few insects have achieved a more wonderful adaptation than *arion*. Although an oft told tale, it had best be included here, yet again, so that all may realise the intricacies of *arion's* life. The eggs are laid from late June through July, depending on the season, on the flower-heads of the Wild Thyme, *Thymus drucei* Ronn. The small larva, when in its fourth instar, ceases to feed on the thyme, drops to the ground and wanders about. At this point reference to F.W. Frohawk becomes necessary. It must be realised that, in Edwardian times, many collectors had tried to breed *arion*. Ova could be collected, without difficulty, simply by watching a female depositing her eggs on the thyme. They fed up well on thyme flowers and then, suddenly, they fell to the bottom of the breeding cage and nothing the harassed entomologist could do tempted them to take nourishment. So his trip to Barnwell Wold; to the Cotswolds; to Dover or South Devon, which promised so much, all came to naught. Then, one day, a keeper, digging for what he called 'ants' eggs', with which to feed his young pheasants, found in an ant's nest a pupa. He had not seen the like before. Then he remembered a Mr. Frohawk living in the village, who was 'up in these things', and decided to show him his find. It was as well he did, because Frohawk recognised the pupa to be that of a *Lycaenidae*, but much larger than usual. No doubt agog, he awaited the emergence of the imago. It was *arion*!

So now the mystery was solved and it only remained to observe and record the meeting of the *arion* larva and the ant of the genus *myrmica*. This detailed work was done by Capt. E.B. Purefoy and enabled Frohawk (1924) to give an account of the last stage of the larva*. It was seen that the *arion* larva

* See E.B. Ford 'Butterflies' p.114.

was very soon found by an ant which, as is the custom of ants, tickled its find with its antennae. At once the larva produced drops of sweet liquid from the two outlets of the honey-gland carried on its seventh abdominal segment. The ant greedily swallowed the honey and continued to do so for up to an hour when, suddenly, the larva assumed a very strange attitude, puffing up its front sections and displaying a convenient gap between the third and fourth segments. The ant now straddles the larva and, finding the gap exactly suited to its jaws, picks up the larva and carries it off to its nest, doubtless hoping to use it as a milch-cow for several weeks to come. Such is not to be; for the larva, as soon as dropped, scuttles down a passage into the depths of the nest in quest of young ant-larvae. Having found these, it feasts upon them until early May, broken by a long winter sleep from October to February. It pupates in a chamber in the ant's nest and emerges after three weeks. It is, of course, wingless at this time, but plentifully covered with white hairs. These offer it protection against the ants as it hurries upwards along the crowded corridors. Into the sunlight it goes, up the nearest blade of grass and there it expands its glorious blue wings. *Arion* has arrived! A story of marvellous adaptation, specialisation, and co-operation; meaning that for much of its life the larva is not exposed to the threats of parasitisation, of trampling, of fire, of being eaten by birds or of cannibalism.*

So what is the snag? Why was it always rare, and now extinct, in Britain? Like all intricate matters, everything is fine until something goes wrong. Its like the German Army — everything planned with care; there was nothing ad hoc about Von Moltke. Then something goes wrong and improvisation is required. The German soldier finds this difficult, but to the British it was normal. That is, until General Montgomery arrived on the scene, when things had a way of going to plan!

Obviously, with *arion*, no ants meant death; no substitute was possible. I have no record that genus *myrmica* became any

---

* Cannibalism is not uncommon amongst the *Lycaenidae*, which attack and eat one another without compunction.

less attentive than before. Are there times when, for some reason, the ants kill their honey-sweet guests? Perhaps a distraught nurse-ant hurries up from below, shouting that another three of her babies have disappeared. A search is made and the culprit found. But wait a minute — the 3.2 mm long honey-giver has grown into a 14.8 mm bloated, shiny, pinkish white monster. A fearsome object and probably safe.

Having realised the intricacies of *arion's* life, it is not surprising to learn that the insect was always considered to be rare in Britain. Let us just see what authors of butterfly books thought about it from the middle of the last century onward. I will start with W.S. Coleman, not because he ranks particularly high in the butterfly cognoscenti, but because he wrote in 1860 and I happen to own a copy of his book. This came to me through my great-grandfather, who bought it from, or was given it by, a certain Thomas Landon in 1901. My great-grandfather left it to my grandfather in 1923 and the latter immediately gave it to me that same year. I was then aged sixteen and already intrigued by the ebullient throng of our native butterflies.

Writing about *arion*, Coleman says that, next to the Mazarine Blue, *Cyaniris semiargus,* it was our rarest butterfly. He gives the following localities for it — Barnwell Wold, Brinton, Shortwood near Cheltenham, Charmouth, Dover, Glaston-bury, Marlborough Downs, near Bedford and near Winchester.

Writing in 1893, F.O. Morris adds Chatteris in Cambridge-shire and Bolt Head in Devonshire. In 1921, Richard South quotes Stephens (1828) as saying it was 'an insect of great rarity'. Stephens gave Bedford, Winchester and 'rocky situations in North Wales' as localities. South, himself, writes that *arion*, in 1921, was only to be found in limited numbers in the Cotswolds and West Cornwall, and no longer at Clovelly in North Devon. In 1945 E.B. Ford* wrote that *arion* was still to be found in North Cornwall and North Devon and one or two localities on Dartmoor. My old friend, the late Baron de Worms*, had,

---

* Butterflies by E.B. Ford pp. 126-7.
* Proc. Brit. Ent. Nat. Hist. Soc. Vol 6 p.1.

previously, found the butterfly plentiful on 23 June 1933, in thick bracken and heather, at Millook, south of Bude.

I now come to very recent times and rely on T.G. Howarth* for an account of the final years of *arion* in north Cornwall. I must point out that Mr. Howarth says (1973) that there are rumours of the butterfly occurring elsewhere, but I can find nothing, subsequently, to support such rumours. In 1964 a survey of the area between Tintagel and Clovelly showed that the number of populated sites had dwindled from thirteen to ten. By 1968 this number had fallen to two. In 1970, these last two remaining sites provided only 31 sightings during the whole season. As this figure was arrived at without marking the specimens, the total may well have been less. It marked the finish of the species in Britain, officially announced in 1979.

Mr. Howarth mentions myxomatosis as a possible cause of the decline, since rabbits undoubtedly stopped gorse from spreading unduly. Gorse and thyme are not compatible. But he also states that, long before myxomatosis, *arion* sites had been kept secret, jealously guarded with no collecting, and yet the insect had disappeared. I do not believe that blaming collectors is a satisfactory explanation for its disappearance and turn to Thomas and Lewington (Butterflies of Britain and Ireland, 1991) for an explanation. They consider that changing agricultural practices, allied to the loss of the rabbit, meant that the turf grew dense and tall.

Tall, shaded turf is fatal for *Myrmica sabuleti*. Its disappearance is quickly followed by that of *arion*.

In 1982 a Mr. John Lodge claimed that he had found colonies of Large Blue in the Cotswolds, the Hebrides and many other places. He refused to show these sites to anyone and so it became known as the 'Lodge Blue'. There is no official support for any of his observations and I have heard nothing more of the matter. To show what people thought at the time, I give a cutting from the Daily Mail of 13 February 1982 as an Appendix to this chapter.

* Proc. Brit. Ent. Nat Hist. Soc. Vol 5 pps. 121-126.

It was in late June 1958 that I first tried to see *arion* in its Cornish coomb. I knew that, by this time, I would not see it at the Baron's site — Millook. So I decided to work north of Bude. I, of course, knew about the thyme and the ants, and I knew it favoured south-facing banks. Between Bude and Hartland Point the coast runs north to south. Therefore the coombs, running down to the sea, would tend to run east to west, giving a south facing bank on one's right hand walking seawards. I took along a one-man tent, a cooking stove, rations for three breakfasts and, of course, a bedding roll. Some miles north of Bude, on the evening of my arrival, I motored round until I found a farm not far from the cliff top. I knocked on the door and a delightful, elderly farmer appeared. I asked him if I could put up a small tent in one of his fields. 'Of course, my dear' he replied. Somewhat shaken by this term of endearment, I thanked him for his kindness and assured him that I would leave no rubbish. He enquired if I wanted any water. I told him I had a jerrycan of the stuff in my car, whereupon he insisted that I took some milk. Such hospitality to a wandering 'bug-hunter' is not all that common, and I left with a warm glow upon me. I only wished the weather was equally warm. I supped in a local pub and turned in early.

I cooked a breakfast of bacon and eggs and washed it down with scalding tea. Then into the car and off to find a coomb. It started to drizzle and, though I found several likely looking coombs I, naturally, saw no *arion*, which only flies in sunshine. A pub-lunch and then off again on my search. No joy. The same dull weather greeted me the next morning. This time I revisited the coombs I had discovered the day before, deciding to look carefully on the tall grasses for any roosting *arion*. I had remembered that the Chalk-hill Blue, *Lysandra coridon*, could be found this way in dull weather. Again, no joy. So, after lunch I packed up, said a grateful farewell to my kind host and returned in 'empty-handed dejectedness'* to Hampshire.

---

* A term used by Peter Scott, in his book 'Dawn Chorus', to describe his feelings after yet another failure to bag a wild goose.

Over the months that followed I tried to learn more about *arion*. The few people, who had seen it on the wing, were, rightly, not prepared to give details of its locations. But I did learn that the best time to see it was between 9 and 12 o'clock in the morning and that it was only active in warm sunshine. I also thought that I might have been too early. As a result, I made plans for another try in 1959. I would stay with a friend of mine in Dulverton (Somerset) for night 6/7 July, and leave early 7 July for the north Cornish coast. I would take my friend along for the ride. Having made this arrangement, I stipulated that the weather had to be warm and sunny.

In the event, the summer of 1959 was just this throughout its length. Accordingly, the early morning of 7 July found us prospecting in the area of the village of Welcombe. We hoped the name was propitious. At 10.10 hours, walking along a path at the bottom of a steep-sided valley, I saw my first, real, live *arion*. I caught it and released it — it was a very worn male. Soon we saw many more; a vivid display of beautiful, blue forms. The greatest density was where the thyme was most plentiful, but there was much movement away from it. The males flew much faster than the females, which were noticeably larger, except, in one instance, when I caught a dwarf female. She was, presumably, the result of a larva being picked up by the wrong genus of ant. It is difficult to judge the number of butterflies in a colony, unless marking is resorted to. However, my friend and I both made independent running counts, which, surprisingly, arrived at the same number — between seventy and eighty. In a fine summer such as 1959 we were too late; the females were fresh, but the males were mostly worn; the first twenty-two we caught were all released.

By 11.15 hrs the flight stopped and no more were seen until 17.15 hrs, when we watched a particularly large female ovi-positing. The day was very warm and sunny throughout. We camped that night with my kind farmer of the previous year. Next morning we searched neighbouring areas from 09.00 hrs and saw area (a) 1♀, area (b) 1♀, 2♂, area(c) 3♂. We left at 11.00 hrs for Dulverton; my friend with some lovely photos and I with a few specimens to grace a cabinet.

Next in the fly-past comes the Chalk-hill Blue, *Lysandra*

coridon. Still plentiful on chalk or limestone down-land in southern England, it flies the last week of July to the third week in August. Like many other butterflies, its numbers at a particular site are subject to massive fluctuations. The astonishing varieties achieved by this species are notorious: there is a whole book 'The British Aberrations of the Chalk-hill Blue Butterfly' by Bright and Leeds, 1938, published on this subject. I have it before me as I write and note, amongst the 82 original subscribers, the name 'Lipscomb, Captain C.G., 5th Batt, Nigeria Regiment, Laria, N.Nigeria, West Africa'. So long ago, and so far away, the lure of butterfly variation had gripped him'*.

Originally, it was the great *coridon* colonies of Dorset, Sussex, Wiltshire, The Chilterns and, especially, Royston in Hertfordshire, that attracted the variety hunters. Here, in the first week of August, the aficionados would assemble, morning after morning, to patrol their special beats. Woe betide the newcomer who trespassed on that little fold in the Downs, the 'property' of old Dr. Black; or that patch of thyme reserved solely for the use of the irascible Mr. Gotcher-Lysandra. This close scrutiny of the *coridon* colonies produced a wealth of varieties, all of which had to be named. Obviously the var '*roystensis*' got its name from the place; and '*fowleri*' must be eponymous. But a strange, quasi-scientific nomenclature was produced for the remaining 698 vars listed by Bright and Leeds. Thus the forewings are 'anti' and the hindwings 'post': both left wings are 'sinis' and both right wings are 'dex'. From this you will readily understand that 'antisinis-postdex' means left forewing and right hindwing: this phrase preceding such a definition as 'discoidalisnulla', meaning 'without any discoidal markings', would describe a very rare form indeed! It must have been fun inventing such remarkable names and, to my delight, I was able to join the game. In August 1984 I was wandering on a Hampshire down, when I saw, and caught, an unusual looking female *coridon*. On closer inspection I found it to be very unusual. On reaching home I hurriedly consulted

---

* The late Maj-Gen C. G. Lipscomb, CBE, DSO, already referred to as 'Lippy'.

Bright and Leeds, so as to name my prize; but in no way could I match it. Accordingly, I named it '*anticaecastriata-postfulvescens*' and showed it at the annual exhibition of the 'British Entomological and Natural History Society' held in London in October of that year. Here my specimen was duly photographed and appeared in the 'Transactions' of the Society, with the remark 'possibly unique'.

To me, the most interesting part of this find was the fact that this *coridon* colony was very low in numbers that year, I believe I only saw 8 specimens during my walk. Yet, amongst them was this rarity; while in previous years, when *coridon* was present in thousands, I had seen only a few of the commoner aberrations.

Of course, Lippy loved to hunt for *coridon* vars. Indeed, he had retired to the Wylie valley so as to be close to large colonies of the butterfly. His collection of *coridon* specimens was amazing — drawer after drawer of named varieties. I was amused to notice that he had marked out the drawers as had been done in the stamp album of my school-days — squares labelled with the type of variation to be placed there. By the time of Lippy's death there were very few empty squares and all is now in the British Museum (Natural History). My regret is that he did not live to see my prize *coridon*. I would have taunted him with it and he would have twisted my arm to possess it. Doubtless I would have given in, as I had done with lesser finds in the past.

One final word on *coridon*. It is now generally agreed that *coridon* vars are no longer found in such numbers as were seen in the twenties and thirties. I have heard some querulous complaints about this; but it has always struck me that the relentless removal of aberrations from the *coridon* colonies for year after year must also have removed the genes responsible for variation. Thus today, although the colonies are, on average, of much the same size as in the past, variations are hard to find.

Closely allied to the last species is the Adonis Blue, *Lysandra bellargus*. So close, in fact, that they have been known to inter-breed! They both share the same food plant, the Horseshoe Vetch, *Hippocrepis comosa,* and, thus, the same habitat. However

Adonis Blue

bellargus is much the more local of the two and I, personally, have never seen them flying together. Of course, *bellargus* is double-brooded, flying in May and again in August, and so it is only in August that the two species could meet. I first saw *bellargus* on the Downs, near Winchester, one perfect, sunny May morning in 1956. The blue of this butterfly is brilliant; it compares with any blue that tropical butterflies can produce, even the famous *morphos*. It is the blue of a noon-day summer sky with a shine to it that dazzles. No painting can really do justice to it and I was privileged, indeed, that day in May to see *bellargus*, in great numbers, flying over the warm, scented turf of St. Catherine's Mount.

The different, often subtle, hues of the British 'Blues' can really only be fully appreciated by comparing them, preferably in sunlight, side by side in a cabinet drawer. To my eyes (and you are free to say I should see an oculist) our other 'blues' are (male only, unless female specified):-

(a)	Chalk-hill blue	-	Silvery, moon-light blue
(b)	Holly blue ♂	-	Mauve-tinged blue
	Holly blue ♀	-	Lilac blue
(c)	Common blue	-	Same as Holly blue ♂
(d)	Silver-studied blue	-	Violet blue
(e)	Large blue	-	An iron blue, with a metallic sheen. Sexes alike

I am told that conservationists are worried about the future of beautiful *bellargus*. Doubtless it has its ups and downs, like *coridon*. For myself I have notes that it 'absolutely swarmed on 16 August 1983 on Ranmore Common, Surrey'; and that 'I saw it in great numbers on Brook Down, I.O.W., at 10.00 hrs. on 21 August 1976'. I have not recently been on the Downs and so give no up to date personal comment.

Both this species and *coridon* have some apparent dependence on ants. In both, their larvae have glands exuding sweetness, and are often attended by ants. Though in no way so dependent on ants as is *arion*, ants appear to play some part in their lives.

Next we come to the Common Blue, *Polyommatus icarus*, and common it surely is; inhabiting the whole of the British Isles, except the Shetlands. It is mostly double brooded and, in the Scilly Isles, even treble brooded. To me, the interest of this species lies in the remarkable variety of the female upperside. Of course, the underside of *icarus* is as liable to aberration as is *coridon*, and in the same style; but I have never found it so commonly.

Of the female upperside, var *caerulea* is the most striking. I have only seen it once and that was on Cotley Hill, Wiltshire. I must point out that normal females of *icarus* are basically brown coloured. They may, or may not, have some blue scales, and normally have a border of orange coloured lunules on both upper and lower wings. When I first saw *caerulea* I was about to pass it by as a male; then I noticed it was heavy bodied. I netted it. It was a female, with wings as bright a blue as any male, but with a vestigial border of small, black dots.

In Scotland I have twice seen dark blue females, with only faint lunules, but with very noticeable white blotches on the underwings. E.B. Ford does not consider that there is a Scots race of *icarus*, but points out that there are *icarus* sub-species in Ireland and in the Scilly Isles. For subspecies to form, isolation is essential and perhaps this is not possible in Scotland. But funny things happen there. For instance, in England, the Chaffinch, *Fringilla coelebs*, calls 'Spink Spink'; in Rothiemurchus it has a different call — more like 'Jock Jock!'

We come now to a species full of interest — The Holly Blue, *Celastrina argiolus*. It is the only British butterfly where different broods use a different pabulum; the spring brood larvae having fed on ivy bloom and the summer brood larvae having eaten holly-buds. Other sources of food have been quoted, but the two I have mentioned seem to be the commonest. The point to note is that the larvae eat the flower buds and not the leaves, so holly can only be used in the spring. Fortunately, ivy blooms in the autumn. While on the subject of pabulum, I believe the spring flight can lay its eggs on *pyracantha* species and, although I have seen the butterfly spend much time on the flowers of the Snowberry, *Symphori carpos*, I have seen no sign of ovi-positing.

The second point of interest is that the females of the summer flight are markedly different to those of the spring

66

flight. Not only is the background blue different, but the black border is greatly extended. I have failed, however, to note any differences in the males of the two broods.

Is this difference in the female due to change of diet; to temperature changes; or to some selective process of which we have no idea? And why in the female only? One realises that, as far as butterflies go, changes are more frequent in the female; consider *valezina* females of the Silver-washed Fritillary and *helice* females of the Clouded Yellow. Quite a few questions here.

Yet another point of interest in considering *argiolus* is the remarkable population explosions that occur. These are not local affairs, but cover many counties. In 1990, the species swarmed in both broods in my part of Oxfordshire (first seen 28 March) and was seen in some London streets. Again in 1991 it swarmed (first seen 8 April). In 1992 it appeared very late (21 April) and in really small numbers in both broods in my area. In some areas it was hardly seen at all. The possible causes of fluctuation in butterfly species are climatic; parasitism; loss of habitat. Parasitism seems the most likely in the case of *argiolus*.

Taking very little room in the Fly-past comes our smallest butterfly, the Small Blue, *Cupido minimus*. It is also taking very little room here, for I have little to say about it. I used to find it year after year in a little hollow on Stockbridge Down. I saw it no-where else on that Down and its numbers stayed amazingly constant. Of course, I have come across it, occasionally, elsewhere; but my impression is that this little butterfly is not as common as it used to be. It is easily missed, however, being confined to small, tight-knit colonies as I found at Stockbridge. Here I used to watch it flying with the Five-Spot Burnet, *Zygaena t. palustrella*, as I looked for varieties. I never saw one, but enjoyed the sight of the gaudy Burnets amongst the rather drab Small Blues.

At last we come to the end of a long chapter, and its subject is scarcely a Blue; it is the Small Copper, *Lycaena phlaeas*. Again, I have the feeling that this little butterfly is not as common as it was in my youth. The larvae feed on dock and sorrel and, in our present over-clean and tidy countryside, these plants are not welcome. Long ago an elderly road-man used his scythe to keep our lane-sides reasonably tidy. He was slow, and he did not get around to cutting them too often, bless him! Nowadays the County Council sends a tractor, with a most efficient cutter, to shave our roadsides. He appears not twice a year, but monthly, to remove the wayside flowers, which so delighted us, and the butterflies; to leave a swath of brown, mildewed rotting vegetation to offend our sight. Pressed years ago by a local Natural History Society, I wrote to the Hampshire County Council complaining about all this. I agreed that the verges, either side of road junctions, needed frequent attention; but pointed out that the school children who, we were told, were without pencils and books, would greatly benefit from the savings obtained by cutting down heavily on verge maintenance. Even small lanes, once the haunt of the Common Whitethroat, *Sylvia communis,* and Yellow Hammer, *Emberiza citrinella,* are cut so often that the insects needed to feed the young of these species are there no more. Neither are the birds. There is no need to destroy the roadside vegetation like this. Just one good shave in the autumn (except at road junctions) would do the trick. Think of the money saved; think of our happy children sucking their pencils; above all think of the swarms of brilliant Small Coppers, and other butterflies, to delight their parents!

Before leaving *phlaeas,* the question of how our native butterflies survive our damp, ignoble winters might well be considered. *Phlaeas,* itself, survives our winters as a larva. Of interest is the fact that this larva may be in its last instar or very small. Thus, the emergence of the first, spring brood of *phlaeas* is protracted. Much the same happens with *aegeria,* as explained in a previous chapter, but for a different reason.

In an Appendix at the end of the book I show how our butterflies pass the winter — either as ova (O), Larvae (L), Pupae (P) or Imago (I). The more superficial of my readers will have remarked how the totals add up to 56; whereas we have only 55 native butterflies. Ha-ha, they will have said, what about that Smarty-pants? S-P replies that there is one species which winters either as a larva or a pupa. It therefore appears in two columns.

I have long studied this chart, hoping to find a clue as to whether wintering behaviour is a factor governing the viability of a species in our climate. I have only found contradictions.

Appendix

Daily Mail, Saturday 13 February 1982

BUTTERFLY WARS

Is the Large Blue really still fluttering or is it just a flight of fancy?

by June Southworth

In this Year of the Butterfly it should be a cause for celebration when a dedicated naturalist swears he's seen the Large Blue alive and well and living in the Cotswolds.

But the eminent entomologists who declared that butterfly extinct in 1979 say John Lodge is engaging in a flight of fancy.

In fact, with the amused contempt scientists reserve for amateur enthusiasts, they refer to his sighting last summer as The Lodge Blue.

To a man who lets moths nest in his best suit this is tantamount to treason.

'How dare they trumpet the death of this beautiful British butterfly with such seeming gladness', says this retired schoolmaster who regards the outdoors as his classroom. 'And then refuse to admit they jumped the gun!'

Mr Lodge runs a one-man nature reserve at Maldon in Essex, and has a group of young enthusiasts called Wilderplors who go on trips with him.

A shy bachelor with blue eyes and fluttering hands, he says earnestly: 'The Large Blue is alive on three sites in the Cotswolds, one in the Hebrides, and many more places I'm sure. It's a shy and secretive creature, you know, quite wonderful. I have a rapport with it.

'You mustn't stomp over the grass the way some of these experts do. It's easily frightened away.

'One day I'll gently catch one and film it, then perhaps they'll believe I can tell one butterfly from another.'

Identification is not always sure, with at least half-a-dozen blue butterflies in the field. The Large Blue has a yellowish-buff underside and a striking powder blue upperside, with a block-black fluted pattern on the wings with spots of the same colour. It has a fascinating life-cycle.

The eggs are laid on thyme plants when they are in bud, and when the caterpillar falls to the ground it is picked up by foraging red ants and taken back to the nest, where it lives the life of Riley. While the ants milk it for a liquid secreted from its gland, the caterpillar dines off the ants' juicy brood.

Then as a chrysalis it stays in the nest for about four months, emerges underground as a butterfly and crawls to the surface, where it flutters around delightfully for about five days.

'I've seen it all happen,' claims John Lodge. 'You see the ants dragging it to their nest.

It's wonderful! They *allow* it to eat the brood. And when the ants' built-in barometer tells them the good weather is here, they want to spring-clean the nest so they go up and touch the folded wings.

'The butterfly emerges and crawls to the entrance. The guard ants which could tear it to shreds don't molest it. They watch it go out.

'I've had an ant-hill apart. I understand their ways. I've watched them for weeks.

'Eight years ago, way off the beaten track, in the Cotswolds, the Wilderplors and I saw a lovely blue butterfly with a rather slow flight and thought it was a Large Blue.

'Then we saw a caterpillar the colour of the wild thyme buds — pinkish-brownish — being dragged along to an ants' nest.

'I swore the children to secrecy. 'Don't even tell your parents'. And for eight years they've kept the secret! They've been with me tending the ant-hills every season, and we saw the Large Blue again last year.

'I've seen them in the Outer Hebrides. And I've had letters from other enthusiasts who confirm they've seen the butterfly on my sites.

'Do you know the latest? The experts are planning to bring over Large Blue eggs from the Continent to breed here. When we've got our own Large Blue. Would you credit it?'

In 1979, the last Large Blue colony under official observation disappeared, and the Government's Nature Conservancy announced the butterfly was officially extinct.

The World Wildlife Fund suggests kindly that perhaps the Lodge Blue is, indeed, the genuine article that has escaped from a butterfly farm.

'Although it sounds daft,' says Mark Carwardine of the WWF', it's possible to say something is extinct and still keep an open mind. If John Lodge filmed it, that wouldn't prove anything. It could be a Continental one.'

Without doubt, John Lodge's greatest stumbling block is a brilliant entomologist, Dr. Jeremy Thomas, whose work for the Institute of Terrestrial Ecology prompted the official view that the Large Blue has breathed its last in the British Isles.

'John Lodge seems to have an answer for everything,' he says. 'There's a site in the West Country that sounds promising, but the claims for the Cotswolds seem extremely unlikely.

'He's always claiming he's just seen unusual butterflies no one else has observed. I can say emphatically that he didn't see the Large Blue last year.

'The descriptions are all wrong. The young caterpillar is a third the size of an ant and one ant could run with it to the nest, whereas he talks of it being dragged there...his anthills are made by yellow ants because red ants don't make anthills

'All his sightings have been very, very late in the season, though they're bang on for the very similar Holly Blue.

'He doesn't want anyone to work on his site and I can understand that, but unless we see the butterfly how can we support him?

'He talks about this butterfly being very sensitive, then he takes children tramping over the site and even holding the butterflies in their hands.

'Then he talks about us being glad to say the butterfly is extinct. That's absolutely maddening. We've spent years looking for it and hoping. We were incredibly sad to announce that all colonies known to us had gone.'

71

Back to John Lodge.

'They seem to have an answer for everything. Escaped from butterfly farms, yellow ants...it's like Comedy Playhouse. They'll say anything to spike my guns!'

STREAKING

To many people interested in our native butterflies, the Hairstreaks, sub-family *Theclinae,* will always have had a special appeal. We only have five species of these delectable little butterflies in Britain and their main attraction is that they need looking for. Three of them pass much of their time in the upper branches of tall trees; another at the top of high blackthorn thickets and only one lives at eye-level. All will be clear later.

Their name derives from the thin, white lines which adorn their undersides. They also sport tails — sometimes a vestigial second tail occurs. Variation in this sub-family is very rare; when it occurs it is usually due to the enlargement or diminishment of the 'hairstreak'.

There may be some scientific reason to put these five species in some particular order; but I am dealing with them in the order in which they charmingly introduced themselves to me. Thus I first came in contact with a Hairstreak when staying at the Wynnstey Arms in the little village of Llanbrynmair, in Mid-Wales, in May 1934.

One morning, probably in search of curlew or snipe, I crossed a damp, boggy field. Halfway across I stopped and, suddenly, found myself in the centre of a mass of little green butterflies. They were everywhere in the bright sun, flying close to the ground and quite unconcerned at my presence. There were no bushes in the field — just grass and rushes as far as I could see. Never again have I seen the Green Hairstreak, *Callophrys rubi,* in such numbers.

Much later I was to see this Hairstreak flying round bushes of dogwood on St. Catherine's Mount in Hampshire, and on similar bushes growing on Salisbury Plain. Indeed, the Plain is home to many colonies of this and other butterflies.

The green colouring on *rubi* is confined to the underside and the 'hairstreaks' can be well defined or, very commonly, represented by a couple of dots. I have no experience of *rubi* larvae but have read, with interest, E.B. Ford's* account of the unique ability, amongst British butterflies, of *rubi* pupae to make a noise.

In 1955, to the right-hand side of the Stockbridge—Winchester road, stood a fine wood. It had plenty of mature oak; some stands of tall spruce; huge beech trees and an interesting undergrowth of thorn, sallow, hazel etc. It was the home of three pairs of willow tit; a colony of hawfinch; a few woodcock and the usual delights of nuthatch, tree-creeper and golden-crested wren. The heart of the wood has been removed and replaced with cornfields. For what? For money. Money is quite nice but, as the Beatles sang, it can't buy you love — it can't buy you hawfinches either.

Wandering, one sunny morning in July 1955, in this paradise I came to an oak-shrouded glade. Glancing up at one of the tall oaks I saw many, dark-coloured, small butterflies flying about the top-most branches. I knew enough, even at that time, to realise that I had a Purple Hairstreak, *Quercusia quercus,* colony in my sights. But I only had a distant view, because they never came lower and so the beautiful purple colour on this butterfly remained invisible. It was this frustration which led me to devise what I have called the 'Schwartz-Metterklüme' method*. This requires two people to operate it. One person arms himself with a few 18-inch long billets of wood and the other takes up a position about 40 yards back from the tree. Fortunately *quercus* seems to favour trees which look upon an open space and so this second person, equipped with a butterfly net, has a good view of the proceedings. When all is ready the 'billet-man', who must have a strong arm, hurls a billet to the top of the oak. Sooner or later a billet will strike a small branch and so frighten the

* Butterflies by E.B. Ford, p.92
* I acknowledge the incomparable 'Saki'.

74

Green Hairstreak

pants off master *quercus,* who is busy breakfasting on honey-dew; *quercus,* doubtless thinking a bird has landed on his branch, at once flies outwards and downwards, at great speed, to hide amongst the leaves of a suitable small bush. The thrower can not see, exactly, where the butterflies have gone, but the long-stop is admirably placed. He has about five minutes to box a few *quercus* before, one at a time, their panic vanishes and they fly back to oak-top once more.

It was thus that I first examined this beautiful little butterfly in all its glory!

Incidentally, the glory lies chiefly with the female. The male's purple is dull and suffused. Later, on a July day in the New Forest, I was to see *quercus* in such swarms that it was not only at the oak-tops, but on all the branches down to eye-level: the S-M method had had its day!

I leave *quercus* on a sombre, but not sad, note entitled:'The Death of a Butterfly'.

The Death of a Butterfly

This day, 22 August 1962, was one of the few, warm, sunny days of a dreadful August. A female Brown Hairstreak had hatched in my study on 21 August. I put it in a pill-box and at 1430 hours 22 August I went out with my youngest son, aged 9, to release her at the spot where I had found her as an egg. This egg, and 24 more, I had found in September 1961, by watching her mother lay on little, stunted sloe bushes on the edge of Kimpton Down Copse, two miles from my Hampshire home. All through the long, cold winter of 1961/62 this minute white egg had remained glued to the sloe-twig, on which I had found it, in my cellar. In May, when the first young leaves appeared on the sloe bushes, the egg was placed in warmer surroundings. Soon the very small caterpillar emerged and took its first meal of sloe leaf. It throve, turned into a chrysalis and then to the perfect butterfly. I released her at the exact spot where I had first seen her mother. She fanned her lovely, orange and black wings several times and then took her first flight. With astonishing speed she mounted to the top of a tall oak tree; the same tree to which I had seen her mother fly after a bout of egg laying. A remarkable fact.

While watching the oak tree, to see if I could see my Brown Hairstreak again, I noticed a dozen or more Purple Hairstreak flying round the top of a neighbouring oak.

Soon I saw some much lower down, and shortly took two very worn females as they sipped nectar from bramble blossoms at the foot of the tree. When released they quickly mounted to tree-top height. Then, suddenly, I saw one Purple Hairstreak start coming earthward. It pitched on oak leaves several times, but seemed not to have the strength to hang on to the leaves, shaken by a brisk breeze. Slowly it fluttered ever lower and collapsed in the grass at my feet. I let it cling to my finger and examined it. It was a very worn and tattered male. He fell from my finger and expired in the grass. I imagine the sight of his fellows, playing in the warm sunlight, had made him try one last fling. But old age had caught up with him: he just had no strength left in his little body.

So his short, gay and charming dance of a life had come to its appointed and apparently painless end. How seldom, I wondered, can anyone have had the opportunity of witnessing the death, from old age, of a tiny butterfly.

I have already mentioned the Brown Hairstreak, *Thecla betulae,* and it is now its turn to face the music. To face the music and dance. The trouble with this butterfly is that it dances at the top of oak trees in far fewer numbers than its purple brother, though sometimes in his company. Like *quercus* the female is the brighter marked; so much so that the ancients called the male the Brown Hairstreak and his mate the Golden Hairstreak — two butterflies for the price of one! I have never caught a wild-born male *betulae;* it is most secretive. However, the gaudy female descends to lay her eggs on small, rather straggly sloe-bushes, growing at the edges of a wood, or along the side of some little-used country lane. She is then vulnerable, but had best be left to her business.

It was thus, one sunny afternoon, that I was assisting my young sons as they flew a model aeroplane on Kimpton Down. Ever watchful for bugs I saw one, then another, unusual butterfly flying from a rough hedgerow, across the Down, towards the oaks of Kimpton Down Copse, half a mile away. Intrigued, I searched the sloes in the hedge and soon found several white ova placed at the junction of a thorn with the twig. The leaves were on the bushes and searching was not easy. A friend, Sir Reginald Maxwell of India fame, and then President of the Andover Natural History Society, told me to wait till November for *betulae* ova and then to search the small sloe-bushes growing besides the many, grassy lanes that flank the Plain in the Tidworth area. This I did, with success, and so had the pleasure of rearing many of this charming creature. I achieved this, largely, by sleeving the larvae on some damson trees in my orchard. The resultant imagos were far larger than their wild parents: what their wild brothers and sisters made of them, when I released them back from whence they came, I do not know. This I can say; the present strain of Tidworth *betulae* produces butterflies no bigger than they always were.

Having had much experience in rearing this Hairstreak, I think it appropriate to mention its pupation methods. They are remarkable, even wonderful. I should mention that Hairstreak larvae much resemble a small slug. One never sees the head, nor the feet, of this humped enigma*. When the time comes to pupate the larva takes up a position under the sloe-leaf, which it nearly covers, and, after a day or two turns into a brown pupa. This lies parallel to the leaf, unsupported by any silken bands about its midriff, relying solely on the fact that the larval skin, itself bound with silk to the leaf, stays attached to the tip of the pupa and thus holds it in place. I have said that this is remarkable, and it is the more so when one realises that the vast majority of butterfly pupa retain no vestige of larval skin. Indeed, such retention would jeopardise the safety of the pupa. Just consider the Purple Emperor's superbly cryptic pupa*. Here, the larval skin, if retained, would prejudice the effect. Along with this, another minor

---

* Its body has serrated edges exactly to match the serrations on the rim of the sloe leaf. Clever!
* See chapter 'Purple is for Caesar'.

miracle occurs: how, if you are hanging by your toes to a leaf, do you shed your skin and still remain hanging by your toes? Knock twice and ask for Iris!

Next to streak into view is the White-letter Hairstreak, *Strymonidia w-album.*

Its larva, at least in Britain, feeds on the elm and, more commonly, the wych elm. The disease, which has, more or less, eliminated both these trees in recent years, has meant that *w-album* has been hard pressed to survive. The wych elm put up a better fight than the common elm, but, branch by branch, over the years it finally succumbed and, with it, its little colony of Hairstreaks.

I found my first colony of *w-album,* by chance, at 4.10 pm on the hot afternoon of 11 July 1956 in Harewood Forest, near Andover in Hampshire. I was, doubtless, on the prowl for vars of the Silver-washed Fritillary when I spotted two or three little black triangles seemingly attached to the purple flower-spikes of willow-herb, which grew plentifully in that place. Approaching, in some excitement, I saw the tell-tale W mark, etched in white upon the dark underside of a small butterfly gorging itself on nectar. I was thrilled; a new butterfly, a new bird, a new girl — of course one is thrilled! If not, Sir, then why are you alive?

Having boxed one or two I looked around to see whence they came. At a short distance was a clump of four, very tall wych elms and, what is more, flying around the crowns of these fine trees was a lively company of small, dark butterflies. *W-album* is smaller than its cousin *quercus* and I was in no doubt that I had found a thriving colony of my new butterfly. For several years after this I was able to take friends to see *w-album* at his high-tea. I recorded, at the time, that it seemed that he only came down on the willow-herb in the late afternoon of very warm days in the first half of July.

Talking of high-tea, reminds me of the young man at a cocktail party. He noticed a remarkably pretty girl, all alone and without a drink in her hand. He straightened his tie and went across to her. 'Let me get you a drink' he said. 'Ectually,' said the girl in a terribly affected voice 'A don't drink'. 'Oh well, have a canapé'. 'Thenk you, but ectually A don't eat'. He produced his cigarette-case. 'Thenk you, but ectually A don't smoke'. 'What' said the youth 'do you do about sex?' 'Ectually, we usually have tea about sex'.

I only once bred *w-album*. Long after my Harewood colony had gone, I found a small line of wych elm on the edge of a Dorset heath. One or two trees were still alive and I beat the lower branches for the larvae of a moth I wanted. In the process the distinctive, slug-like larva of a Hairstreak fell on to the tray.

I carried it home in triumph and, with difficulty, obtained the right pabulum for it. It became a larva of prodigious size and produced an ultra female the following July. It dwarfs my wildlings and people enquire as to its provenance. I only say that I gave it the care and attention I give all my larvae.

I cannot leave this species without referring to the wonderful var obtained by my friend Lippy. Any variation of the Hairstreaks is both rare and minimal. But he found a *w-album* with the W so greatly enlarged as to make the underside of the insect almost unrecognisable. Its photograph graces the Proceedings of the Brit: Ent: Nat: Hist: Soc!

I have left the rarest of the streakers to the last — the Black Hairstreak, *Strymonidia pruni*. In May 1957 I went up to London to visit the Nature Conservancy Headquarters. I went in order to plead my case for a permit to take a few specimens of this very rare insect in Monks Wood, a locality in Huntingdonshire and an ancestral home of *pruni*.

I was asked why I wished to possess *pruni*. I replied that I would, one day, write a book about our native butterflies and could not do that without seeing them alive and without being able to study them after death. I was given, most courteously, a permit to take 6 specimens in the Monks Wood reserve. Now, 36 years later, I am writing that book. Don't ever rush people!

So, armed with a permit, I went to this sacred grove. I quote verbatim, from my notes made at the time. They are disjointed, but that's the way it is. Although allowed to take 6 specimens, I only kept 5 of the many I caught. Sloe, amongst which this butterfly lives and mates, is very tough on butterfly-wings!

Black Hair-Streak   Went Monk's Wood with permit 23/6/57. Arrived 1300 hrs. Had only 1 hrs. sunshine and had to start absolutely from scratch. Had motored for 4 hrs. and had no lunch. Dashed madly around, as I saw weather was worsening. Looked at all privet on rides. NIL. Then found big sloe clumps on edge of wood and at once saw and caught a v. torn *pruni*. Soon beat 8 more from bushes. Some shot straight up and either settled out of reach or went over top of trees. Caught and released 1/2 dozen v. worn. Next morning arrived 1000 hrs. Raining. It rained until 1.30. At 2.00 pm sun came out and from 2 to 3 patrolled rides. Caught two 'perfections' by beating trees round privet bushes. Only saw 1 (v. torn) actually sucking at privet. Saw many high up I could not reach. One wants 3 people. 1 to beat, 1 with long pole net and 1 with short. I had too short a pole. Dr. Clarke was here on 21 & 22 June. He caught 40 and kept 4 perfectos. Met Mr. Hall (Warden). *V. Cheerful* and helpful. He said a Mr. Wills was coming on 26th. He had come three years without success. Last year it rained all the time of his 3 day visit and he saw *not one.* In fact last year *none* seen at all. This year quite plentiful and *v.* good sport. Typical elusive hair-streak and very well worth while. It seems, like *quercus,* to spend much time high up in oaks, presumably feeding on leaf secretions. This makes it, at times, most difficult to compete with and accounts for its elusiveness. Monk's Wood impressed me by its paucity of sloe. Many woods I know in Hants have *far* more, yet no *pruni.*

I have mentioned the absence of *pruni* from Hampshire and, indeed, it is only to be found in Huntingdonshire, Northamptonshire, West Buckinghamshire and Eastern Oxfordshire. That this comparatively narrow band of Midland territory is its only home in Britain is cause for comment, even wonder, having regard to the wide distribution of the sloe. And here I must digress: never fear, the digression leads back to little, black *pruni.*

One bitter dawn found me, gun in hand, up to my knees in water at the bottom of a six-foot dike, on the edge of a large Lincolnshire field, not far from the little town of Holbeach.

I was waiting for a flight of pink-feet geese, which never materialised. As the sun came up I was preparing to climb out of my trench, when I heard a loud splashing going on just round a corner of the dike. I decided to investigate. Round the corner I went and there beheld a sight fit to freeze my already icy blood. A gigantic wild-fowler, in full winter kit and flaunting a red beard, stood before me, armed to the teeth.

Between us was a pink-foot goose — the cause of all the splashing. It had, somehow, got into the dike and, being unable to spread its wings, could not escape. 'Your bird, Sir' said the courteous apparition. I disowned the honour. 'Then' said the fowler 'we must rescue the goose'. This we did, with no little difficulty. I caught the goose and my new friend opened his capacious game-bag to receive it. He examined it, pronounced it unwounded, and strapped it in his bag, with its long neck sticking out. He introduced himself as James Robertson-Justice. The date was December 1936, and the name meant nothing to me.

James asked me where I was staying. I told him I was at the Chequers in Holbeach. 'Then', said James 'let us get to your pub and give this goose some food'.

The bird must have been in the trench for some time; it was emaciated, but still belligerent. We arrived at the Chequers, fresh from the field, at about 9 am. Mine host was used to fowlers coming in for a late breakfast. He batted not an eyelid until he saw the goose. James asked for a saucer of bread and milk to be placed before the bird, as it sat in the shooting-bag on the fire-mat in the hall. The goose attacked its breakfast with gusto. A matter of wonder. Here was a bird, straight from an Icelandic wilderness, eating in front of a small crowd of humans.

Suddenly, the hotel cat started to stalk this serpentine creature. All it could see was the long neck and head of the goose. It had a big shock coming; because the goose, looking up from its dish, saw the cat and gave it the full anserine hiss. What guts! The hotel guests gave it a cheer.

Over our breakfast James said we should take the bird to his wild-fowling friend from Cambridge days, a man called Peter Scott. Scott, apparently, lived in a disused lighthouse on the

Wash, and kept wild geese, with their wings clipped, in compounds on the marsh, which surrounded that place. He studied the birds and painted their every movement. To this I, of course, agreed. That afternoon we took our pink-foot to Peter Scott. He pronounced it uninjured and accepted it with thanks.

From that beginning I had a friend in James, that traversed a remarkable career. Up or down, he was a lovely companion; full of wit, full of wisdom.

So now we must return to *pruni*. The catalyst is Sir Peter Scott. For some reason, which now escapes me, I was invited to a Luncheon in London. The reason for this was entirely ornithological. I was, to my delight, seated next to Sir Peter. Our meeting was greatly helped by the incident of the pink-foot. After a while our converse slipped from ornithology to entomology. Sir Peter had procured 500 ova of *pruni* from Monks Wood and had put the resultant larvae upon the massive clumps of sloe that grew within his Gloucestershire sanctuary.

He told me that, for the first year, he saw many *pruni*. The second year he saw a few. The third year he saw none. He, being a high-class naturalist, had carefully considered all this, and we discussed it at length. There are problems here that are still unsolved. People have many theories. I leave it at that.

BUDDLEIA BUGS

The buddleia, of whatever colour, has such an attraction for butterflies that it is, at times, covered with their beauty. Thus, it often provides the basis of butterfly knowledge; not only for country-folk, but for suburban dwellers as well. The shrub blooms in July and so coincides with the emergence of some of our most brilliantly coloured butterflies, none of whom can resist the allure of its long, spiked flowers.

Of all the beauties that feast here, the Peacock, *Inachis io,* can be the most plentiful. For instance, one July morning, in 1992, I counted 40 individuals on our large white buddleia*. I think there were more, but there was so much movement that I can not be sure. Yet, in 1993, I saw none in July. I saw a few in the garden in early March and noted seeing one Peacock, at noon on 13 March. It spent all its time feeding and I timed it for twenty minutes on one small patch of alyssum; very different to the Brimstone, *Gonepteryx rhamni,* males, who flew incessantly back and forth all that morning.

After 15 March that year I saw only one more Peacock, although there were many warm, sunny days till the end of the month. This was bad news; because the Peacocks one sees in March are the parents of the swarm one hopes to see gracing the buddleia in July. As I have said, I saw *none* on the buddleia that year. But not to worry. Long ago I found that *io* aestivates, at least in some years.

Of course, it hibernates as well. I recall, one mid-winter in Hampshire, finding a little fleet of *io* sleeping the winter away,

* In the village of Aston Rowant, Oxfordshire

upside down, on the roof of an open-sided garden shed. I call them a fleet, because they looked like black-sailed yachts, sailing, upside down, on a dark, calm sea. There were nine of them and they were close together. I took someone to view my little fleet and, to my horror, could only see seven. I feared for their lives, but could not close the shed. More disappeared and then I saw the pirate. As it passed me, it said (I think) with its mouth full 'Yer've got to live, mate'. It was a common or garden wren! Of course it had to live and, of course, my *io* had to die to this end. It is the utter ruthlessness of Nature that sometimes hits one. But the *io* weren't mine — they were the wren's. Let us press on!

Let us consider aestivation by *io*. Everyone knows about hibernation — from the Latin *hibernus,* wintry. Aestivation derives from the Latin *aestivare,* to pass the summer. In pursuit of this matter I have consulted the Old-Timers. Morris, Coleman, Frohawk, South only mentions hibernation. Even E.B. Ford does not consider the possibility of *io's* aestivation. Yet *io* is an occasional aestivator. In early August 1979 I was searching for a moth called the Old Lady, *Mormo maura.* I was told that this large moth could be found, roosting by day, on the underside of bridges spanning the many small streams, which cross the New Forest in Hampshire. Accordingly, I studied my map and noted where roads crossed these streams. On 3 August 1979 I devoted the day to 'Exercise *Maura'.* To my delight, the second bridge, whose underside I inspected, disclosed two Old Ladies, snoozing the day away. I also noted several *io,* hanging upside-down, on the roof. At first, this made no impression. But, as I visited more and more bridges, I saw more and more *io.* Here was a bright, summer's day in early August and *io* was not on the buddleia — rather, fast asleep on the roof of a damp, dark bridge. Obviously, *io* was aestivating; or do people consider that hibernation starts in late July—early August?

Perhaps, though, the term aestivation should only be used for those insects, like the moth, the Dotted Rustic, *Rhyacia simulans,* which emerges in July, flies for a short time, then retires and reappears from late August to October.

Be that as it may, I am trusting that, in 1993, *io* decided to

Peacock

go into retirement as soon as it eclosed*, and so gave the buddleia a miss. Surely this would be aestivation. The matter will arise later in this chapter.

Before leaving *io* I must record a strange occurrence regarding the Old Lady. On entering a large culvert, which carried a few inches of water, I saw a round object attached to the roof. It was quite big and, on shining my torch on it, I saw it consisted of a mass of large moths clinging to one another. I dropped them into my net and there counted nine Old Ladies. In bulk, they gave off a highly unpleasant smell, which I had never noticed with singletons. They quickly left the net, made for the day-light at the end of the culvert and disappeared into some trees not far away, leaving two of their number for my collection.

Next I choose the Comma, *Polygonia c-album,* to fly down from the buddleia and be examined. In most years, not 1993, this handsome insect shares the nectar with *io*. It is seldom in the numbers of that butterfly, usually being seen in twos or threes.

However, once, in the month of July, I saw it in swarms on bramble blossom in Harewood Forest in Hampshire. All that morning they were busy at the blossom and I noted quite a few of the dark, super-convoluted form amongst them. These do not fly for long, but go into aestivation/hibernation and are not seen again till the following spring (late March-early-April), when they meet their nephews and nieces. These, latter, emerged the previous September, fed for a short time on fallen apples, Michaelmas daisies etc, and then hibernated. A pattern is now beginning to emerge. Let us start in early April, say, when *c-album* leaves his winter hiding place and goes in search of a mate. The result of these spring pairings emerge throughout July. Some of them are of the dark form, already discussed, and the rest of the form which used to be called *var hutchinsoni**.

* Hatched from its pupa.
* Named after a Miss E. Hutchinson, who wrote in 1887 about this lighter, brighter type.

I have tried to find out if there is a normal ratio of light to dark forms in this July emergence. Frohawk found a preponderance of the dark form in a summer brood; others mention only a few. Perhaps the type of summer has an influence. What is clear is that Nature has designed a remarkable insurance against the failure of the September brood: lying hidden is a reserve ready to emerge next April.

I have never heard of the Hutchinson type appearing in the September brood.

Indeed, it is quite unsuitable for hibernation, when compared with the dark type. This, marvellously, mimics a dead leaf, with torn edges. The white comma shows up as a jagged hole in the leaf to complete the deception. All achieved by natural selection!

Like many, very specialised creatures this butterfly seems liable to catastrophe. Such creatures then withdraw to a sort of heartland. Here they recuperate, or not, and start spreading outwards again. *C-album* underwent just such a withdrawal. South, writing at the end of the last century, considered it to be almost confined to the counties of Herefordshire, Worcestershire and Monmouthshire. In 1919, as a boy, I found it quite plentiful in some flowery meadows, in the parish of Hyssington in Shropshire. I well remember showing my few specimens to my Grandfather, who collected here and abroad. I noted, with glee, his obvious surprise at my precocity and his remark that it was a long time since he had seen one. The species was, obviously, on the mend and now is to be found all over the Midlands and the South of England. I have never seen a satisfactory explanation for all this.

Flitting as blithely as a buddleia bug, I now produce, for your delight, the White Admiral, *Limenitis camilla*. You may well say 'If you suppose you're going to see *camilla* on my buddleia, chum, you've got another think'. Of course, you are not so vulgar — but I know what you are thinking!

Yet there are folk, whose gardens are near-by large woods in the southern half of Britain, who frequently see *camilla* on their buddleia. Anyway, where else could I fit this elegant fly.

And elegant it is. None of your common, flapping stuff. With a flip and a skim, a twist and a glide, it soars about the

86

trees or floats the woodland ride. Occasionally it stops at a bramble blossom for a sup, but mostly glides the day away. I have always found it enchanting.

And so is its var *nigrina*. Long hours have I spent waiting and hoping to see this rarity; without success. But success does sometimes follow. Here is an account, as told to me by my friend, Jim Porter, of how he took *nigrina* in the summer of 1993.

'I arrived in a Surrey wood at 12.45 hrs. on 29 June 1993. It was one of the few warm, sunny days of a dismal summer. My hope was to capture *camilla var nigrina*. I have been collecting for 30 years and *nigrina* has eluded me. Perhaps today would be my lucky day.

There were many butterflies about, including *camilla*. I had just netted a fresh Ringlet for inspection. With my hand inside the occupied net he skimmed past my head; the black White Admiral — *nigrina*! I waited at a nearby bramble patch for his return. I waited, long past lunch-time, till 1500 hrs, at the bramble-patch, when I saw *nigrina* dash past; ignoring the bramble blossoms.

I then recalled how the ancients had lured butterflies, by impaling a dead specimen to a bush. The passing males had paused to examine the bait. I would try this. So I caught an elderly, worn *camilla,* killed it with a quick nip and impaled it on a thorn.

I would wait until 1700 hrs. — no longer. At 1659 hrs. *nigrina* suddenly appeared at the bait. My net seemed to move by its own volition — at incredible speed. *Nigrina* was mine. At last — long last'.

I end by describing the astonishing, unseemly beginnings of a lovely butterfly. I have watched *camilla* lay her eggs*. She lays a magical, little orb of palest green on the upper side of a honeysuckle leaf, near the rim. So far, so good. Honeysuckle is a fragrant herb and the egg is a marvel of delicate sculpture — a minute, orange-shaped structure with innumerable raised facets, each reflecting light, so that the tiny egg shimmers

---

* At 1600 hrs, 17 July 1964, in Harewood Forest, near Andover, Hampshire.

under the lens: and lens you must have if you are to view this marvel properly. From this beautiful, jewel-like egg emerges a minute grub*: it has a large black head and a pale-yellow body. It at once nibbles the very edge of the honeysuckle leaf, near the tip. Its whole body heaves with the effort necessary to make the first incision. Slowly the body turns from pale-yellow to dark-green, as food passes down the digestive tract. As soon as the dark colour reaches the hind-most end of the caterpillar (about 8 hours after the first bite) excrement is passed. This is known, in entomological circles, as frass. (My dictionary says this is derived from the German 'fressen' = to eat. I have no quarrel with this. How caterpillars eat!) So far all is normal. Now occurs an unique sequence; at least amongst the larvae of British butterflies. This minute larva makes extraordinary use of its own frass. It not only covers its body with its own excrement, but builds a 'jetty' of its frass and thereon slumbers. All the butterfly-books tell how the small larva of the White Admiral uses its own frass to decorate itself What amazes me, is that none I have read* describe the 'jetty'. Not even Edward Newman, such a careful observer, mentions the matter.

I must go back, a small while, to the passing of the first frass. As soon as this is passed (a minute, pin-point lump of blackness) the larva shows signs of interest. It turns round and examines it most carefully. It nudges it — it tosses it, with its head, like a bull would a matador. Then it leaves it. I, the watcher, with blinking-eye through a high-powered lens, wonder what will happen next. I will tell you. The beast attacks the leaf at another point on its rim and passes more frass. Soon there is quite a bit of frass dotted about on the margin of the leaf. By the twentieth hour after hatching, at least three

* Five days after being laid: but kept indoors in my study.
* I have read South, Ford (E.B.), Ford (R.L.E.), Morris, Edward Newman and Frohawk. Only T.R. Bell, writing of Indian butterflies in papers sent to the Bombay N.H.S. (collected under the title: 'The Common Butterflies of the plains of India') mentions similar traits in the young larva of *Limenitis procris,* a close relative of our *camilla,* which is also of the genus *Limenitis.*

pieces of frass are in position on the larva's body. It places frass by picking it up and firmly fixing it to its body with silk. There is a lot of head-weaving before, during and after the placing of a piece of frass. After six, or so, pieces have been placed in position on the body the larva starts building the 'jetty'. I call it a jetty but, when it goes upwards, it could be called a tower. It is made of bits of frass, firmly bound one upon the other with silk and, after 48 hours, is twice the length of the larva. It may be built in the same plane as the leaf or at any angle up to the vertical. It may be quite straight or it may curve slightly. It may be built at the tip of the leaf, when it appears as an extension to the mid-rib, or it may be at any place on the rim. The minute larva spends much time at the tip of the jetty, asleep. However, as soon as it passes frass, it quickly turns round, seizes it in its mandibles and at once places it at the tip of the jetty. Much work with silk follows and, after five minutes, the jetty is that much longer and stronger. The larva, naturally, does its feeding around the base of the jetty; but, at first, seems to reserve the passing of frass to the time it spends at the tip of the jetty. If all this fascinating enterprise is to be watched, then the larvae (I had two) must be placed on growing honeysuckle as soon as hatched. Otherwise, each change of pabulum* will mean the destruction of the jetty. By the sixth day the larva goes into a trance, at the tip of the jetty, for a skin-change. This is necessary for the growth of the larva, at regular intervals, throughout its larval life. Most larvae do this five times and, as each stage is called an 'instar', they have six instars before turning into a pupa (chrysalis).

Every time the larvae went to a new leaf a fresh jetty was built until fourteen days after birth, when both larvae changed skin for the second time. With this, they also sloughed the frass attached to their bodies. Never again did I see them resort to the strange habit of fixing excreta to their bodies. By this time the larvae had changed leaves at least three times and ceased building jetties. I believe 'jetty-building' ceases just before the second skin change (i.e. in the second instar).

* The entomologist's term for the food of larvae.

In the third instar, the larvae were eating the leaf from the tip, on either side of the mid-rib. The jetty-building, which I thought, at first, must have some relevance to the hibernaculum, appears confined to the first and second instars and to be discarded long before hibernation. In any case, the leaves on which the jetties were built were of no use as hibernaculi, being almost completely eaten away. The young larva needs far more than one leaf for its sustenance. By the age of nineteen days the larvae were 0.25 ins. in length: were clothed all over in spikes and were pale brown — not green. They ate prodigiously — a normal sized leaf was three-quarters eaten within seven days.

On the twenty-fourth day after hatching*, one larva started to build its hibernaculum. In blazing hot weather it set about preparing for the long, cold winter, which lay ahead. Magical stuff — all this. First it chose a very small leaf, on a very short stalk, for the hibernaculum. It first bound the stalk to the stem with silk and then nibbled the top off the leaf. Next it bound the two sides of the leaf together with white-coloured silk, so that the edges appeared *laced* together — there being gaps between the laces. By 18 August the larva had bound itself into a tight-fitting hibernaculum.

The second larva had by 25 August, still not completed its retreat. It started on 20 August by binding the leaf stalk to the stem. But the leaf was a large one and so it ate a narrow cut from the rim to centre rib, near the base of the leaf, and folded the portion of leaf thus left available. But the silk lacing soon stopped and the larva lay in a sort of hammock, fully exposed. It was overcome by its winter sleepiness before the hibernaculum was fully constructed and there it remained without movement.

The appearance of the larva, and its behaviour in the spring, have been frequently recorded. There is nothing new that I can add about *camilla* after its emergence from its hibernaculum. But its first twenty-four days of life do not appear to have been so generally recorded.

* The date was 14 August

Next on the buddleia comes the Small Tortoiseshell, *Aglais urticae*. There is not a lot to say about this fellow that has not been said about the Peacock. It comes out of hibernation in March or April, mates, lays its eggs on nettles and dies. The progeny emerge. They, like all butterflies, can not resist the buddleia. But I have found that it stays longer on the wing than many Peacock do, and is specially addicted to the dark-red flower heads of sedum. This flowers in gardens long after the buddleia blooms have gone, and there are times, in late August or early September, when it is covered with *urticae*. It is, therefore, obvious that this butterfly can put off hibernation until much later than all but the Comma.

This is due to the fact that in the South of England *urticae* is double brooded. Not, I think, in every year. At any rate, in the South-Midlands there are years when the normal June emergence is not apparent. One might suppose that the mating activities of this summer brood would be observed, and so be left in no doubt as to whether there had been an emergence or not. Such, however, is not the case. I will tell you why — they mate in secret.

Like a lot of things in life it came to my notice by pure chance. Have you noticed we always say 'pure chance'? Is not chance sometimes impure? In the same way politicians always make themselves 'absolutely clear'! I should delete 'pure'; it is trite, hackneyed, worn out, abominable. But stet; it has served to remind me to be on guard and has, also, served to keep *urticae's* mating secret for a little longer.

One warm, spring day in early April, many years ago, I was wandering on a sandy heath listening to my favourite British song-bird — the wood lark. Sweet, admirable bird; an ode should have been written to you! In my wanderings I came to a post and rails fence at the edge of the heath. There were many flowers in this place and I noticed an unusual number of *urticae* flying around. Then I noticed one in close pursuit of another. Whenever the leading one stopped on a flower, the pursuer landed close behind and started playing drum-beats, with its antennae, on the wings of the leader. They completely disregarded my close approach and I was able to see they were male and female; the male being the pursuer.

You may think this would be obvious, but in the insect world the male is by no means always the pursuer. For instance, in the case of a moth, the Ghost Moth, *Hepialus humuli*, the white male flies at dusk up and down, like a yo-yo, above the grasses. It takes care to fly with its back to the fading light, so that its ghostly, white image can readily be seen. The large, brown females are on the prowl and, flying straight at this yo-yo, knock it to the ground. Here, mating takes place. 'Oh, what can ail thee, knight-at-arms alone and palely loitering;'* The answer is absolutely nothing!

To return to *urticae*. The pursuit continued until the female flew up to the fence and disappeared into a large crevice, where the upper rail passed through a post. The male was nonplussed and, after hovering for a while, flew off. I waited to see what the female would do. She, obviously, expected mating to take place. She was feeling about, in all directions, with the tip of her abdomen; the rest of her being only faintly visible in the recess. Her wings were folded above her body. After a while she flew off. I do not know what went wrong, but if all *urticae's* courtships ended like this, then it would long ago have joined the Dodo. I am short on the scientific name for this bird; but our name derives from the Portuguese word, Doudo, meaning silly.

And it would be silly here, not to mention two resplendent members of the 'buddleia bugs'; The Red Admiral, *Vanessa atalanta* and the Painted Lady, *Cynthia cardui*. Though not natives of the British Isles they are regular visitors and often plentiful. The Red Admiral was particularly plentiful in 1993, taking the place of the Peacock on the buddleia. Wherever I went in that year I was to see its vivid beauty, from the South Coast to the Scots border. During the first week in September it was particularly plentiful in Cumbria. For a migrant this seems a long haul.

It is pleasant to realise that all the Red Admirals one sees are not doomed to die in this country. Large flights of them have been seen, late in the year, in the English Channel flying south; a return migration. I had long heard rumours of such

* Keats. La Belle Dame Sans Merci

an event, but it was not until I met a farmer-fisherman at the Annual Exhibition of the British Entomological and Natural History Society in 1993 that I had a first hand account. The gentleman was knowledgeable about butterflies and had witnessed this southward movement of Red Admirals many times off the coast of the Isle of Wight. He was adamant that they were Red Admirals and not Painted Ladies. Indeed, he had never seen a southward flight of the latter. This point interested me very much. Here you have two species of very similar habits, yet only one apparently has a return migration.

On the subject of Painted Lady, I was lucky enough to witness a migration of this butterfly in North Africa. On 8 March 1988, between 1630 and 1800 hrs, I watched a steady stream of *cardui* flying northward through the beautiful gardens of the La Mamounia Hotel at Marrakech. The seven-storey hotel itself proved no obstacle; they flew straight over it. The next day, I saw a similar northward movement of *cardui* in the Atlas mountains.

It is obvious that neither *cardui* nor *atalanta* imagos are equipped for hibernation; their undersides are far too brightly coloured. They, therefore, must either over-winter here as an egg, as a larva, or as a pupa if they are to qualify as British native butterflies.

There is talk that *atalanta* imagos have been found hibernating. I am not going to offend people by saying 'poppycock'; but if anyone can prove that *atalanta* regularly passes our winters as an imago, then I will eat a small portion of my old Indian topee; well buttered and with strawberry jam!

ALL WHITE

The title of this chapter might be what a man, who could not pronounce his 'Rs', replied when asked about his health. But, no. It is about our six native butterflies of the family *'Pieridae'*, referred to as 'The Whites'. I would have liked to have included exciting species, like members of genus *colias;* but, alas, they are visitors, not natives. What, in my youth, was known as *edusa* (The Clouded Yellow) had what were called 'Edusa years'. Then one's grandfather took the train to Budleigh Salterton and, while his family did what families did at the Victorian seaside, he lost pounds of weight chasing *edusa* in the sunshine.

Now it is called *croceus* and, with its new name, does not seem to find Britain quite so attractive. I suspect this may be due to the fact that our farmers do not grow lucerne, *M. sativa,* to the extent they used to. So I say 'Au revoir' to *Croceus* and his delightful, though aberrant, wife *Helice.*

Now to a true Brit — The Brimstone, *Gonepteryx rhamni.* I suppose this should be called a 'Yellow' and not a 'White'; but then the female is pale green, so white will hurt no feelings. I put *rhamni* at the head, because, for most people, it is the first butterfly of the year seen on the wing; a true harbinger of spring. For me, however, there remains some mystery about *rhamni* in the spring. Here are some notes from 1993. Admittedly this year was not an average year, too little sun and too much rain. But the facts I give are, broadly speaking, applicable to any year.

'For two days, 13 and 14 March, 3 male *rhamni* continually flying in and out of my garden. They were never seen to feed; but flew up and around, as if forever searching. One presumes the search was for a mate. No females were seen then, or later, until 10 May. Then a female *rhamni* was seen in the garden, continuously feeding. Pansies were the most popular flower used. No males about, nor had there been any seen since one male appeared in the garden on 30 April in very hot weather.'

There were no further sightings of *rhamni*, of either sex, until 9 September, when three males were in the garden, busy feeding.

These dates for 1993 bear out what I have noticed over many years: males appear early (in 1990 on 21 February), fly for a day or two and then vanish. Females rarely seen in April, but frequently seen in May ovi-positing on buckthorn, *Rhamnus catharticus*. Whenever I am searching in July for *iris* ova on the pussy-willow, I keep a look-out for a buckthorn bush. In the Whiteparish woods of South Wiltshire the buckthorn is plentiful and I have frequently seen Brimstone larvae. Often many have been parasitised by a braconid fly. The pupa of this fly is a somewhat gruesome affair. At first sight it appears to be a bird-dropping. On closer examination it appears to be a bird dropping wrapped up in the skin of a caterpillar, because the head and tail of the caterpillar appear at the ends of the pupa.

In most cases the larvae of hymenoptera-type parasites leave the host caterpillar to pupate.

In this case the larva pupates inside the completely gutted skin of the host. It was a few years before I realised that there were two types of fly involved, showing a subtle difference in their pupal markings.* The flies themselves also differed very slightly. I have not found a book which enables me to give their scientific names, but Mandy Shepherd has drawn pictures, which admirably show what I have been writing about.

When first I started breeding butterflies and moths from larvae I was angry when some hideous grub or fly appeared in the breeding cage, instead of the beauty for which I was hoping. I destroyed the foul fiend with oaths and curses. Now, however, it is carefully set up and preserved, with complete data, awaiting inspection by someone who can tell an ichneumon from a braconid and a braconid from a chalcid.

* The differences are probably sexual.

This is esoteric stuff and not as simple as the advice given to someone, who had difficulty in telling a stoat from a weasel*.

But, to be serious, the natural controls on insect populations are of vital importance to all life on this planet, and the hymenoptera-type parasites play an important part. So, for that matter, do the tachanids; insects looking, for the most part, very like the house-fly. Whereas the hymenoptera-type parasite lays her egg, by means of an ovi-positer, under the larval skin; the tachanids, having no means of piercing the skin, lay an egg on the outside of the larva. Should the larval skin-moult now occur, then the parasite's egg goes with it and the larva is saved. It would appear that the tachanids are new to the game and have a lot to learn.

This whole subject of parasitism is full of interest. I, some years ago, bred three wingless parasites, looking like ants, from larvae I found on Salisbury Plain. One wonders how being wingless could possibly be an advantage. Then again, parasitism is not confined to larvae; pupae and ova are also attacked. I once had eight minute flies emerge from the ovum of a Poplar Hawk, *L. populi*.

To return to *rhamni*. Those larvae, which escape being eaten by a bird or parasitised, pupate on the bush and produce a butterfly. The pupa, which stand upright supported, round the middle, by a silken girdle, look remarkably like a curled leaf. Their procrypsis is good; but not, I think, as good as that shown by *iris*. However, it is sufficiently good for many *rhamni* to survive and fly in the hot, August sun. I have seen both sexes on the outskirts of a wood, at this time, in swarms. They were busy at the flowers, filling up with nectar before the long hibernation ahead. This is the time to look out for vars. Such are very rare and usually consist of specimens with orange suffusion on the forewings. Of course, there is always a chance of seeing a gynandromorph*. Then, if you catch it, you can take it up to the Annual Exhibition of the British

---

* Such an old joke, than even I have not the nerve to tell it!
* An individual in which male and female parts develop simultaneously.

EX RHAMNI on
17/7/70 from
whiteparish, WILTS

Ex RHAMNi Larvae
22/7 — 2/8/69. whiteparish, WILTS
Fly and pupae.

Brimstone Parasite

Entomological and Natural History Society in London. There it will be photographed and your cup will be full — Brimful.

Now to the first of the true Whites — The Large White, *Pieris brassicae*. If this was a rare butterfly and not so keen on eating our greens, it would be greeted with delight. It really is a very handsome insect; especially in the summer brood, and, especially, the female. Here, the black tips to the forewings, and the large black dots, show up splendidly against an ivory background.

Brassicae is well able to sustain itself in Britain, but receives reinforcements from across the Channel, often in massive numbers. I have seen one such invasion. It occurred when I was at my Prep school in the village of Willingdon, near Eastbourne, and made such an impression on me that, after seventy-seven years, I can still picture the scene. We were playing cricket, when first a few, then dozens, of large, white butterflies crossed the cricket field. Then, quickly, the mass of the main body arrived. Boylike, we fought them off with our cricket bats; yelling and jumping, we struck-out wildly. Surprisingly, the butterflies seemed to be flying at no great height; but, thick and fast, they came on undeterred. The flight was soon over and I have always regretted that I did not make proper notes of the event. The year I believe to have been 1916, and the date must have been before 1 August (The Summer Hols started on that date). But I have no idea of the frontage of this migration, nor the time of its duration. Forgive me; I was only 8½ years old. In the chapter 'Buddleia Bugs' I have told of Painted Ladies migrating in North Africa. It seems to me the Large White behaved in very similar fashion. Much later in life, I saw a movement of Large Whites in north Cornwall. The date was 8 July 1957, but the individuals were well separated and the numbers small. They were flying north over the sea and I worked out that Ireland would be the next stop. Perhaps the good folk of Waterford found, next spring, that cabbage was in short supply!

To return to my Prep school. I believe the year I give for the Large White invasion, 1916, is correct. I say this because, one Summer Term, I clearly remember, along with my chums, listening one afternoon, and long into the evening, to a continuous rumble of thunder. The weather was warm, but cloudless, and we wondered about this. Next morning the Head Master told us that we had heard the guns from the Battle of the Somme. Now, the date of this battle is 1 July 1916. For us to have heard the guns so loudly meant that the wind was South-East and this wind would have suited the butterfly invasion. All these years I have, somehow, connected the two — the butterflies and the thunder.

I, long ago, committed to memory, the opening sentences of Winston Churchill's chapter about the Somme in his book on W.W.I 'Over the rolling battlefields of the Somme broods an air of the inevitable. Beneath its mud lies the flower of two nations. Never were men and ammunition so plentiful, — nor generals so confident as on 1 July 1916'. Little did I think, in 1916, that I myself, a 'Gunner', would take part in what, I believe, was the heaviest bombardment of the Second World War. I refer to the day-long programme we put down in an operation to clear the enemy from west of the Rhine. It was called 'Operation Veritable'.

I thought, during that day of incessant gun-fire, of my childhood and the guns of the Somme. Doubtless, on the Somme, the traffic was 2-way. But few enemy shells came our way this time, for we had long since won the Artillery battle. By 1939 Hitler had decided that the Stuka dive-bomber would do the work of the Artillery. The RAF removed the Stuka and so Hitler was left a bit short of cover. This meant that many British soldiers survived to chase butterflies, instead of the S.S.

Speaking of the S.S. brings to mind the parasites, which prey upon the Large White. There is no doubt that the larvae of both this, and the Small White, *P. rapae,* do great damage to certain crops. The parasites are, therefore, the 'gardener's friend'. Nowadays, I believe, spray-guns do the work of the braconids. E.B. Ford quotes J.E. Moss when he states that up to 84.2 percent of Large White larvae can be destroyed by *Apantales glomeratus,* whose yellow cocoons decorate the corpses of *brassicae* larvae. It is worth remembering that in destroying *brassicae* larvae with chemicals, the natural control is also destroyed. Man tampers with Nature at his peril. (A dreadful, trite sentence, but I can not think of a better).

Much smaller but, otherwise, very similar, is the Small White, *P. rapae*. Its distribution, in Britain, is very like that of *brassicae;* though it is not found so far north. It, too, has a spring and summer brood, with the summer brood showing much blacker and larger markings. Indeed, so different that Coward states that J.F. Stevens* considered the spring form to be a 'good species' and named it *metra*.

I have always found *rapae* to be more prevalent than its larger relative, though both species receive strong reinforcements from time to time. I wonder if this could not be due to the different habits of the larvae of these two species. J.E. Moss, already mentioned, found that only 18.8 percent of *rapae* larvae were killed by parasites. Ford points out that *rapae* larvae are not gregarious and live in the hearts of the plants. They are, thus, not so vulnerable.

I have mentioned that *rapae* receives reinforcements. I can not forbear to quote from 'Coleman's British Butterflies' (April 1860). He produces an extract from a Kentish newspaper as follows: 'One of the largest flights of butterflies ever seen in this country, crossed the Channel from France to England on Sunday last. Such was the density and extent of the cloud formed by the living mass, that it completely obscured the sun from the people on board our Continental steamers, on their passage, for many hundreds of yards, while the insects strewed the decks in all directions.

The flight reached England about twelve o'clock at noon, and dispersed themselves inland and along shore, darkening the air as they went. During the sea-passage of the butterflies, the weather was calm and sunny, with scarce a puff of wind stirring; but an hour or so after they reached *terra firma*, it came on to blow great guns from the S.W., the direction whence the insects came.'

He later writes 'A contemporary account states that these were the Small White butterflies *(Pieris rapae).'*

I can not leave *rapae* without pointing out how the females, especially in the summer brood, show a soft, creamy surface

---

* In his Illustrations of British Entomology (1827-37)

on the upper wings. Allied to quite an ample, grey shading outwards from the thorax, this gives them a surprisingly attractive appearance.

Brassicae and *rapae* may, at times, be a pest. Do not, however, despise their looks. Old Morris chose to use *brassicae,* before its more gaudy comrades, for the picture he wanted on the outside of his seventh edition of Morris's British Butterflies 1893. Here, on the green-board cover of the book, beautifully painted in gold, is a full-size picture of a female *brassicae.* It really looks very elegant!

We now come to the third, and last member of the genus *Pieris* native to Britain — The Green-veined White, *P. napi.* It is to be found all over Britain and in Ireland it produces an interesting form.

Like all but one of the butterflies in this chapter it is double-brooded; and like all those that are double-brooded, the summer brood shows heavier black on the upper side. It is, however, the spring brood of *napi* which shows the heavier markings on the under-side; the so-called 'green-veins'.

Once, long ago, when staying with a friend in Southern Ireland, we went into a wood in County Waterford to find the nest of the Irish race of the Jay, *Garrulus glandarius hibernicus.* I wished to record its calls. Unfortunately, the Jay is not 'garrulus' near its nest and, in this case, not even away from it. Thus, though we found its nest easily enough, and had close views of the birds, there was nothing to record. The eggs are indistinguishable from the British Jay, but I had hoped to show there were voice differences. I dare say there are, but I have no personal proof.

In recompense, I suddenly realised *napi* was in spate. I caught a couple, with difficulty, as I had no net. Their undersides were typical of the Irish race, bright and strongly marked on a yellow background. For the record, the date was 24 May 1965.

This interesting little butterfly is not a marauder of your cabbages. Its larvae, however, savage your nasturtiums in late August and September. Be sparing of them; they will produce butterflies in April, when there are not too many of their ilk upon the wing.

If *rhamni is* the harbinger of the spring then, surely, the Orange Tip, *Anthocharis cardamines,* is the harbinger of summer. I have noticed, over the years, that when I see my first *cardamines* in late April or early May, then it is a sure sign that a warm spell is on its way. The Cuckoo, *Cuculus canorus,* may signify that 'Summer is i' cumin in', but *cardamines* shows that warmth, at last, has arrived.

This colourful butterfly, once so plentiful over Britain as far north as mid-Scotland, is now much reduced in numbers. I put this down to the constant destruction of its main food plant 'Jack-by-the-Hedge', or, in less rustic terms, Hedge Garlic, *S. officinale.*

This slender plant is now mercilessly cut down by County Councils everywhere in Britain. In my youth the country lanes were tended by elderly gentlemen with scythes. They took their time to get around to cutting down all the roadside flowers. They gave time for butterflies to breed and for birds to raise their road-side nestlings. Now a man, sitting in the cab of a yellow tractor, trundles along our lanes, with a sort of mowing-machine attached to the end of a long, jointed arm. This arm is devilishly contrived so that it conforms to the contours of the lane-side, whether it be flat or banked. As it passes, it leaves a swath of grass and flowers slowly to rot to a brown, mouldy mess. In this mould lie many *cardamines* larvae, their lives finished. In case anything might have survived, the yellow monster returns every month to repeat the dose.

I am, of course, aware that the verges, either side of road junctions, need frequently to be cut. But why have our minor roads and lanes to be shaved monthly during the summer? Lovely wild-flowers perish, as well as insects, and all without necessity. When one considers the total acreage involved throughout the country, then the damage caused to wild life can properly be assessed. I, further, realise that men, employed by county councils to keep our roads free of ice and snow in winter, can not be left to twiddle their thumbs in summer. So they are told to shave our roadsides of all their beauty every month. Only road junctions need this treatment; for the remainder an autumnal visit to the barber is all that is necessary. I rebel for *cardamines* and many hedgerow birds.

In the hope that somehow, somewhere, some 'Jack-by-the-Hedge' may be left standing, I go out at the time the Bath and West Show is being held and search for *cardamines'* eggs. My friend, Lippy, told me this was the time to try; when the thin, pointed eggs had turned bright orange and, thus, could easily be seen. The eggs are laid, one to a plant, on the stem of a flower, or on a seed-pod. The larvae are vicious cannibals and so, if two eggs happen to be laid on one plant, only one larva will survive.

The larvae are easy to rear, provided they are kept one to a box, and I enjoy seeing them take up their positions for pupating. Come late April, in the following year, I bring the pupae into the warmth and then release the imagos into the country-side. At the same time I raise two fingers into the air: my salute to the abominable road-man, or not-yeti.

Now to the last of the Whites and, perhaps, the most interesting. It is the Wood White, *Leptidea sinapis*. A hundred years ago it was well scattered, but local, over England, from the New Forest to near Carlisle. Long ago it ceased to be found in Cumbria, probably due to over-collecting, and in the early part of this century withdrew to what might be termed its 'homeland'; in South Devon and Hereford. Now, rather similar to the Comma, *P. c-album*, it has, like young Lochinvar, come out of the west and, though I have not seen it in the New Forest, is really quite plentiful in certain Surrey woods and occurs in what might be termed the 'pruni-belt' — the woods from Northamptonshire, through Buckinghamshire into Oxfordshire, where I see it regularly.

I made my first acquaintance with *sinapis* in Surrey. My eldest son, a boy of fifteen summers, was at school in Godalming and I had asked him to find out where I could see *sinapis* in his neighbourhood. He said he had a friend, who was 'into bugs'; but it would cost me! By this he meant that the pair would expect a slap-up lunch. Accordingly, on the morning of 2 June 1956, I picked up the two incipient businessmen and lunched them at an hotel on the Hogsback. Suitably fuelled for the arduous work ahead, they guided me to Dunsfold Wood. This was a dark, broad-leaved wood, with thick undergrowth. It was crossed, here and there, by broad, grassy rides. At once I was aware that the Small Pearl-Bordered Fritillary, *A. selene,* was 'in spate'. It flew, in numbers, down the rides. In such numbers that my son, having robbed me of my net, was able to catch five in one short dash. He returned the net to me, apparently alive with butterflies! They were released and we turned to the business in hand — *sinapis.*

It was not long before the boy who was 'into bugs', shouted,'There's one', and sped into the trees. I had not seen it, and was delighted to welcome him back with a male *sinapis* in his net. It showed the bright, black blob at its wing-tip, typical of the first-brood. I was interested before; now my interest became intense. In no time at all I saw another cross the ride and disappear amongst the trees. I spurned the help of the two boys and emerged lower down the ride, with my trophy; a female. She was altogether paler than the male, though her body was slightly more robust. We kept one female and five males from our visit to this wood, all in perfect condition. It was my first series of a new species and I was obviously, if not 'over the moon', at least somewhat carried away. I see that I wrote the following in my diary:- 'This wraith like butterfly flies its wavering path through the undergrowth rather than over the rides'. Written nearly 40 years ago, I stick by it!

In later years I was to take some of the second brood in Northamptonshire in late July. They make an interesting comparison with the first brood, being markedly smaller. Thus, whereas *brassicae* and *rapae* are both larger in the summer brood, *sinapis* reverses the order. Which reminds me of the Confidential Report written by a C.O. about his latest subaltern.

'When this young officer joined my Regiment I endeavoured to impress upon him the importance of putting work first, games second and women third. During the course of the year he has persisted in reversing the order'.

On this poignant note the last of the Whites fly past.

SKIP FOR JOY

Coming up fast, and flying low, is the last squadron in the Fly-Past; the *Hesperiidae*. They are known, colloquially, as the Skippers and, as such, are well named. Their darting, rapid flight is diagnostic. In addition, some of their habits are more like those of moths than butterflies. For instance, their method of carrying their wings, when at rest, is sometimes very moth-like. Their pupae are enclosed in a cocoon, unlike those of any other British butterfly; and there are many other, rather technical, features about them, which contribute to their uniqueness.

In Britain we have eight species of Skippers, divided into six genera. The males of all the species carry androconia*. In three species the scent scales are enclosed in a fold of the costa on the forewings and, in the remainder, they form a diagonal line across the forewings. The subtle difference in the 'sex-mark' between the Essex Skipper, *T. lineola,* and the Small Skipper, *T. sylvestris,* was not detected until 1890!

I start with the Dingy Skipper, *Erynnis tages.* This butterfly has a very large range in Britain. It is found throughout England and Wales, much of Scotland and, also, in Ireland. Everywhere it goes it is still dingy; in no way does its viewer, on first seeing it, shout his triumph to the skies. If he catches his breath, it is because he has just climbed a steep bit of downland.

The fact that it has a very interesting larval and pupal existence can, in no way, compensate for its consummate dinginess. I hasten to its companion in sub-family *Pyrginae* —

* Scales specialised for distributing the attractive scent of the male.

the Grizzled Skipper, *Pyrgus malvae*. This species is also a downland dweller, but is not found as far north as *tages*. It is brightly marked, with white dots and dashes, on a brown background. These white markings can vary considerably, leading to some interesting varieties. When, on some bright, sunny May morning, one finds oneself in their company, it is well worth spending time looking out for the rare var *taras, Bergstr,* in which the spots on the fore wings coalesce and form a large blotch. In both these species, the androconia are carried in a fold in the costa of the forewings.

Next on the list are the three members of genus *Thymelicus*. Let us start with the Small Skipper, *T. sylvestris*. Like all this genus, the male carries androconia in a dark line across the forewings. It is not quite parallel to the costa.

This butterfly is exceedingly common. Wherever long grasses, plentifully intermingled with flowers, grow beside a lane, or in a corner of waste ground, there one is likely to find it flying in the sunshine of July and early August. I have long noted how all the Skippers seem greedy for nectar: so that flowers are an essential part of their habitat. They are none the worse for this.

One July day in 1888, the year following Queen Victoria's Jubilee, a Mr. F.W. Hawes, busy with his net in Essex, caught quite a few *sylvestris* (then known as *A. thaumas).* On getting home he realised that three members of his booty appeared slightly different. At the time, he considered them as vars of *sylvestris,* and it was not until January 1890 that the 'Entomologist' recorded them as *Pamphila lineola,* The Scarce Small Skipper; the first time what we call the Essex Skipper, *T. lineola,* was recognised as a British resident. Of course, collectors rushed to examine their collections and soon it was realised that the new Skipper was to be found in a great many parts of Essex, chiefly along the coast.

The Essex Skipper differs from *sylvestris* as follows:
(i) Sex mark much thinner and parallel with costa.
(ii) Underside of antenna black rather than orange.
(iii) Hind wing underside paler and without orange flare.
In planning my butterfly 'jaunts' for 1957, I pencilled in the Essex Skipper, and thought there could be no better place

to try than the sea-walls north of Shoeburyness, towards Foulness. I knew this area well, when stationed at Shoebury in the mid-thirties; though then my interest had been wild-fowling round the islands of New England, Havengore and Potton. I recall magic nights under the moon, with widgeon fluting their exciting flight-calls as they came in to feed on the zostera grass.

Accordingly, on 15 July 1957, I left London by road for Great Wakering, just north of Shoeburyness. For reasons I cannot now remember, it had to be this date and rotten weather it was. I arrived at 10.30 hrs. to find a grey, cold day with intermittent drizzle.

To my concern, I found all the sea-walls had been raised two feet, following the disastrous floods of three years before. This process had completely bared the walls on the land-ward side. However, I saw a small stretch with some grass on it and went there. Not a butterfly to be seen. I beat the tall grass in desperation. After twenty minutes I saw something plop into the grass. Down on my knees, a rapid search, and there was a torpid *lineola*! I saw the pale hind wings and black antennae in a trice.

Five minutes later I got another. It was very slow work. Fortunately, at 13.00 hrs. the drizzle stopped and, though the sun never shone, it became brighter and warmer. Now *lineola* was not torpid and, when disturbed, flew a few yards. I caught fourteen, including one female. I kept 5 ♂ and 1 ♀ all in superb condition. I was, later, glad to have these few Essex specimens for comparison with specimens I was to find in Hampshire, Wiltshire and Oxfordshire. I note, from my diary: 'Drizzle restarted at 15.00 hrs. Came home wet, but happy'.

It was shortly after this that I learnt there was a colony of *lineola* not far from Middle Wallop in the county of Hampshire. I went there, one sunny morning, and found *lineola*, flying with *sylvestris,* beside a cart-track through a cornfield.

I was to find, in subsequent years, two or three more *lineola* colonies on the Hampshire-Wiltshire border. Now, living in Oxfordshire, I have found *lineola* colonies along the foot of the Chiltern escarpment, and elsewhere in the County. The great thing is to catch *sylvestris* type skippers wherever you find them; let them protrude their antennae through the net and, suddenly, they show black undersides. I am sure this is a politically incorrect way to go 'butterflying', but, if you want to find *lineola,* that, as the parrot said, is the way to do it.

All my Hampshire, Wiltshire, Oxfordshire specimens are markedly larger than the true-blue Essex type. I have long wondered how this trim, little butterfly escaped notice until the observant Mr. Hawes decided to take his net out that July day in 1888. Could it be that it only flew on the Essex coast? Or could it be that it flew in many other places, unrecognised and ignored?

E.B. Ford, writing in 1946, gives a distribution map of *lineola,* ignoring many of the sites at which I, and many others, now know the butterfly can be found. I have a great respect for Ford and the care with which he sifted his evidence. There is, therefore a prima facie case for supposing that *lineola* is in the middle of a remarkable expansion of its British range. Just study Ford's map of 1946 and, 48 years later, its present known distribution. Skippers come and Skippers go (see under *palaemon),* but I am glad that I will never again have to grovel in the grasses that grow on the sea-walls of Havengore.

We now come to the last of genus *Thymelicus* — The Lulworth Skipper, *T. actaeon.* The male shows the typical 'sex-mark' carrying the androconia. The butterfly is slightly smaller than the other two species of this genus and a very nippy flier. It was first discovered in Britain* in 1832 near Lulworth Cove, in Dorsetshire, and was thus eponymously named.

Lulworth, however, is not the place to go to see *actaeon.* There are two reasons for this. First, you are liable to get shot, as Lulworth is a tank-range. Second, the butterfly can more easily be seen elsewhere. The butterfly is, and has always been, a very local species, confined to a few places on the coasts of Dorset and Devon. Writing in 1860, W.S. Coleman, considered

---

* The discoverer was J.C. Dale, who took his first specimen at Durdle Door, just West of the Cove, on 15 August. How about re-naming *actaeon* 'The Durdle Skipper' a fine, rustic name; especially if you speak Dorset. As E.B. Ford, in his 'Butterflies', points out, the data is with the original specimens at Oxford.

that the Burning Cliff, near Weymouth, was *the* place for *actaeon*. So to the Burning Cliff I decided to go; greatly helped by a sketch-map my Grandfather had left in Coleman's book. This map showed, clearly, how to get to the upper slopes of the cliff.

On 7 August 1956, I went with the late Lt.-Col. Sam Kirkaldy and my eldest son, then in his early 'teens, to the Burning Cliff. I had always thought the cliff got its name from some massed, red-flowering plants, which might have given the impression, to someone at sea, that the cliff was on fire. Actually, I later learned that shale-oil, at the foot of the cliff, had caught-fire in the mid eighteen hundreds and had steadily smoked into the present century. Like so many of us, it has now given up the habit.

We arrived in bright sun-shine at the cliff top, following my Grandfather's sketch-map, at 10.30 hrs. We walked down the cliff towards the sea, and I pointed out to my son that he was the fourth generation of his family to tread this path.

He seemed not too impressed because, just then, we reached the coarse grass growing on the weedy slopes, which dropped down to the beach. With a shout of '*actaeon* stations' he dashed ahead and caught a male Lulworth Skipper! The place swarmed with them. In an area the size of a tennis court I estimated three dozen of the insects were flying. I saw two pairs 'in cop' and so the date we chose, for that year at least, was just right. I wrote in my diary 'Pleasant to record that, after 90 years, when locality discovered, the fly still so abundant; and we had left many, many acres of 'skipper-land' unexplored.'

Our next customer, the Large Skipper, *Ochlodes venata*, is widely distributed in England, Wales and the Scottish Lowlands. The male has a very well developed sex-mark. As I have nothing of further interest to add, I had better stop and proceed to consider the far more beautiful and interesting Silver-spotted Skipper, *Hesperia comma*.

This lovely, little butterfly is confined to a few, usually steep, chalky areas in the South of England, where the steepness of the terrain, allied to the rapidity of its flight, make it a target only for the more agile of the fraternity. There is no doubt that its present rarity has largely come about due to the ploughing up of much downland for a meagre crop of barley. The Government of the day bribed farmers to plough this age-old land, whose turf, and its flowers, had slowly developed through the centuries. Now the present Government, subservient to Brussels, tells farmers to 'set-aside' land, because nobody wants what they are growing. 'Set-aside' as you please, but the downland will not come back in your life-time; nor that of your son.

Much of the downland had been ploughed in north west Hampshire, where I lived in the fifties and sixties. The Cirl Bunting, *Emberiza cirlus,* suffered when the juniper bushes, growing on the downs, were grubbed-up, prior to ploughing. They provided nesting-sites for the Cirls. But the chief sufferers were the downland butterflies and moths.

Let me pursue this matter. In April 1928 I was sent on a 'gas' course to Porton, in Wiltshire. This was the normal lot of the junior 'wart'*. In working hours I learnt gas-drill by heart and can still, sixty-six years later, remember it verbatim. Its opening lines were: 'On the order "gas", if the rifle is not already slung, place it between the knees. Place the closed fist of the left hand on the bridge of the nose and, with the right hand, knock the steel helmet forward so that it falls, and is caught, on the left arm by the chin strap'. etc., etc. I can do this in Urdu too, but will spare you.

When parades were over, in the beautiful, scented spring evenings, I walked the downs towards what is now the double carriageway of the A30 west of Lopcombe Corner. If you drive this road westward you will, if you look out of your right-hand window, see cornfields.

In 1928, this was downland, with juniper growing everywhere. One evening I put up a pair of Stone Curlew, *B. oedicnemus;* saw several cock Stonechats, S. *torquata,* and found a Long-eared Owl, *A. otus,* sitting on eggs in an old Magpie's, *P. pica,* nest in a thorn-bush. Now it's barley! I was only 20 and had a lot to learn; I have no doubt that the Cirl Bunting was present and I would have been thrilled, had I but known its song.

* A second-lieutenant

By the mid 1950s, when I had retired to the pleasant, little Hampshire village of Fyfield, a few miles west of Andover, one of the few bits of ancestral downland remaining was Broughton Down. This Down is so steep that no Government bribe could induce a farmer to risk his machinery in its destruction. So, when in August 1957 I went to this Down, I was hopeful of seeing *comma*. I was not disappointed. It was flying on the steepest part of the hill and its silvery spots seemed to help in its disappearing act. There you would see a Skipper in flight and, then, as it settled, would be nothing. I went annually to this Down in August, just for the pleasure of watching *comma*.

It had other attractions in due season. Various Burnets, *Zygaena;* Chalkhill Blue, *coridon,* and, in June, the Hobby, *Falco subbuteo,* among the pines that grow along its ridge. I trust it remains unspoilt.

Near where I now live, at the foot of the Chilterns, I was delighted to see *comma* once again enjoying the August sun. Due to its habitat requirements *comma* will always be a local butterfly, perhaps even rare.

I have left to the last the Chequered Skipper, *Carterocephalus palaemon* Pall. At the time when I went in search of it, the butterfly was present, in England, in a narrow band of the Midlands from southern Lincolnshire through Northants and Rutland to Buckinghamshire. It was always a very local butterfly and so was only found in a few woods in these counties. Writing in 1893, exactly one hundred years ago, Morris gives the following woods where what he called 'The Spotted Skipper' could be found; and, often, in great numbers. Sywell Wood, Monks Wood, Castor Hanglands, Gamlingay in the Midlands; Dartmoor in Devonshire and Luton in Bedfordshire. He finishes by saying: 'I have heard that in one of these places the "Lord of the Manor" has forbid the "free warren" and "free entry" of the Entomologist, but I am unwilling to believe that any such interference with the "liberty of the subject" has been perpetrated.' And so say all of us!

In 1957 I decided to have a try for *palaemon*. I picked the wood known as Castor Hanglands, in the Soke of Peterborough, and obtained a permit from the Nature

Chequered Skipper

Conservancy to take six specimens. I arrived at 17.00 hrs. on 15 June in blazing sunshine. Three quarters of the wood had been felled by the Forestry Commission and planted with young pine. The Nature Conservancy had a piece of the wood furthest from the road. I went into this part (mixed Oak and Ash) and at once saw and caught a male *palaemon* in a broad ride. I caught one more and left to book-in at a hotel in Peterborough for the night.

After supper I strolled round the town and took a fancy to the stone walls of the Cathedral; never had I seen so many fossils jammed so tightly together! Next morning I awoke early to a lovely surprise. My cheap, little room was high up in the hotel and the window looked out on to the roofs of the town. Through the open window came the unmistakeable sound of the song of a Black Redstart, *Phoenicurus ochrurus gibraltariensis.* I had got to know this song well whilst in Germany, where the Black Redstart is common. In many parts of the Continent it takes the place of the Robin, *Erithacus rubecula,* which there breeds in the woods rather than in the barn.

After breakfast I asked the owner if I could be shown the way on to his roof. He lent me a young fellow who quickly showed me the way on to the roof and there, in no time at all, I got a view of a cock Black Redstart. I waited for some time, hoping he might lead me to a nest and so enable me to record a breeding record for Peterborough. But all he did was fly from chimney to chimney and claim his territory in song.

By 10.00 hrs. that day, 16 June, I was back in the Hanglands. Another scorching day. I saw about a dozen *palaemon*. Like all Skippers, they flew fast and were not too easy to follow. Having already taken two males the previous day I could only take another four specimens. I, obviously, needed a female but, although the males had, clearly, been out some time, I saw no females. So I had to be content with a bag of six males, some of which were not as immaculate as I would have liked. I noted that the insects were very scattered and looked, in flight, like Duke of Burgundy Fritillary, *Hamearis lucina.* Indeed, I came across a nice colony of *lucina* amongst the *palaemon*. Large Skipper, *Ochlodes venata,* were also present in numbers.

On my way home, I decided to digress slightly and look in on Salcey Forest, south of Northampton. Although by now the heat of the day was over, I was delighted to find quite a few *palaemon* flying in the first ride I came to. And, to complete a golden trip, there on a lovely summer's evening, I caught two female *palaemon*. They are larger than the normal male and their forewings are more rounded. In addition, the upperside markings are larger and so tend to give the female a paler appearance.

From my experience in these two woods in 1957, I would say that *palaemon*, at that time, was in good nick. But, in under twenty years, it was to become extinct in England. It would be easy to point a finger at such as I; but you would be wrong. Remember that the Nature Conservancy had wardens in some of *palaemon's* haunts and that a permit to take a few specimens was only given under special conditions. The cases of *palaemon* and the Large Blue, *M. arion*, are strangely similar, particularly in respect of dates and of protection.

It is of interest to see what entomologists had to say about *palaemon* in recent years. The references, which follow, are to the 'Proceedings of the British Entomological and Natural History Society' unless otherwise stated. In Vol. 12, 1979, p. 101 the late Baron de Worms, writing the obituary of Dr. Kettlewell, mentions one expedition in 1928 to see *palaemon* at Bedford Purlieus on the Great North Road north of Stilton. Frequently, in his writings, the Baron reports that the object of his visit 'was in spate'. No such comment this time. R.P. Demuth, writing in the Entomologist's Record, Vol. 96, p. 267, records how he and Kettlewell, on 3 June 1928, visited Bearshanks for *palaemon*. They found it very scarce. They put this down to 'a lot of men from the village with nets who arrived as we left. Xxxxx's (name of well known professional deleted) toadies I suppose.' The President of the Society reported (Vol 8, 1975 p. 62) that *palaemon* had been confirmed in small numbers in the Midlands. In Vol 11, 1978 p. 50, J. Heath stated that 1976 was the last, and worst, of a series of drought years; for the last three or four years walking in Monk's Wood in light shoes had become possible, owing to the drying out of the soil, though previously, this had not been so. Probably the local extinction of *palaemon* was attributable to this cause.

A.E. Stubbs, of the Nature Conservancy Council, stated in Vol 15, 1982 p.7, that *palaemon* was not positively seen in England after 1975. This leads one to an attempt to account for the extinction in England of the charming, agile Skipper — *palaemon*. All it seemed to require was a grassy, woodland ride, on which grew various flowers, including bush-vetch and, especially, the grass, *Bromus asper.* These conditions were admirably met in the many isolated woods, which were the remains of the old Rockingham Forest. It seems appropriate to point out that another English butterfly, the Large Blue, *M. arion,* became extinct in Enland by 1979. Perhaps only coincidence; but worth noting.

In Vol. 14, 1981, pp. 82-86, T.S. Robertson examined possible causes for the extinction of *palaemon* in England. He considered two factors to be of importance. First, the long-term north-easterly contraction of range, possibly due to climatic changes; the other due to a series of changes in the habitat of the Rockingham Forest. He did not consider that collecting[*] was a contributory factor; the decline being too general and protracted. In trying to be objective, and to give all points of view, I must mention the Pheasant, *Phasianus colchious.* In the British Journal of Entomology and Natural History Vol. 2, 1988, p. 9, a paper by David Corke of the N.E. London Polytechnic argued that it was reasonable to conclude that pheasant predation might be a significant cause of *palaemon's* decline.

Martin Warren, writing in the same Journal, Vol. 2, p. 196, disagrees.

Both views are ably argued and should be read in full. I take no sides. I merely point out that there are many facets to this matter.

In my view loss of habitat (including alterations due to climatic changes) is the most probable answer. Man, of

* But take note of the professional and his 'toadies' at Bearshanks; and the generally accepted view that professionals exterminated the New Forest Burnet, *Z. viciae,* in England in 1927.

course, has been responsible for the extinction of many birds, and it might pay us to consider how he accomplished this. In doing so, there might be some clues as to butterfly losses.

First, let us consider flightless birds. New Zealand has quite a few, and it was not long before the early Maoris disposed of the gigantic Moa *(Dinornis)*. Similarly, the first settlers on Mauritius rapidly knocked the last Dodo on the head. Then, much more recently, the Great Auk, *Alca impennis,* became extinct. This bird was a large, flightless member of the Razorbill genus, which stood, penguin-like, a full thirty inches tall. It laid a single egg. In the 18th Century it was conservatively estimated that one and a half million birds nested on the islands of Hamilton Inlet, Labrador, alone. There were also large nesting colonies off Newfoundland and Iceland. Wintering flocks, off Florida, were once counted in millions. Yet by 3 June 1844, there was only one pair left, plus an embryo within its egg-shell. Allan Eckert in his book 'The Last Great Auk' says 'The two stately birds waddled ashore on Eldey Island off the south coast of Iceland. Soon afterwards the female laid an egg there. Fate has always been fickle, but it was seldom more capricious than on 3 June 1844. (A boat, carrying six men and three boys, landed on Eldey Island from a ship anchored off-shore. The men started clubbing the crowds of birds, mostly Murres, too slow to leave their nests). Suddenly one of the men glanced up and spied the huge forms of the two Great Auks. 'Garefowl' he screamed. Swiftly the men spread out and advanced on the two birds with their clubs at the ready. The birds, on land, were sluggish and awkward. The clubs streaked down. One of the men, intent only upon the Great Auk's fleeing form, stepped on the single, large egg and crushed it. He had just destroyed the last of a species. Thus it was on 3 June 1844, the Great Auk became extinct from the face of the earth.'

And, unless you think that it is only flightless birds that man can destroy, consider the story of the Passenger Pigeon, *Ectopistus migrator ius.* Richard H. Pough, in his Audubon Bird Guide, gives the facts of the amazing story of this extinct North American species. Probably no other bird has ever occurred in quite such huge concentrations as the Passenger

114

Pigeon; their vast, migratory flights darkened the sky and took hours to pass. One great nesting in Wisconsin, in 1871, covered 850 square miles and contained 136 million nests. As late as 1878, one and a half million birds are known to have been sent to market by railroad alone from the last great nesting. They made very good eating. The last wild specimen was shot twenty-one years later, in 1899, and the last survivor, a bird hatched and reared in captivity, died in Cincinnati Zoo in 1914, aged twenty-nine. Thus, from flights estimated to consist of about two billion birds in 1860, no living member of this species existed fifty-four years later. The moral, if any, is that no species, man included (a species reckoned at five billion), can rely solely on numbers for its continued existence.

How does this avian review bear upon the regional extinction of a butterfly species? First of all, the extinction of the Passenger Pigeon was due entirely to loss of habitat. Vast acres of corn, planted by Man, replaced the endless scrub-lands of the Mid-West. P.P.* had nowhere to go. The Great Auk had no protection against sailors, hungry for protein to augment their weevil infested biscuits. Greatly increased shipping was its doom.

In both cases Man was to blame.

The first by actual attack on the individual; the second by farming. Man is the culprit. But is he the culprit if the main cause of extinction is climatic? Some will say he is the cause of climatic change, and so responsible. 5,000,000,000 human beings! Perhaps that is the short answer. (If you call nine noughts short).

The saga of *palaemon*, however, is not done. In 1939, near Loch Lochy, a Miss Ethel Evans took a *palaemon* specimen, which is now in the Royal Scottish Museum. Its date — 18 June 1939. According to George Thomson, in his 'The Butterflies of Scotland' (A Natural History) 1980, James Joycey and A. Noakes had reported seeing 'a Skipper' at Glenshian, in Inverness-shire in early July 1907. As this is a locality now known to contain *palaemon* colonies, Messrs. Joycey and Noakes probably did, in fact, see a real, live Scots *palaemon*!

* Poor Pigeon.

Why the long delay from the first clue in 1907 to its final acceptance as a Scots species, following the finds of Lt. Col. D.W. Mackworth-Praed on 10 May 1942?

I think the answer is due to the often very circumscribed extent of a colony; the size of the country and a dearth of entomologists. George Thomson (ibid) writes 'By the early 1970s, it was thought that the species was on the verge of extinction in its English localities and in the Inverness-shire sites from which it had been recorded.' However, it is now known that many more localities, both in Argyllshire and Inverness, exist. New colonies are being found annually and it is clear that *palaemon* is far more widespread than was previously thought. My personal searches for *palaemon*, in his Scots habitats, have been confined to three trips. All were pleasant (how else? — considering the beauty of the country).

It has always amazed me how so many Scots are prepared to leave all this beauty and wander the world. Two Englishmen were talking and one remarked how seldom he had met a stupid Scot. Of course, said the other, all the stupid ones stay at home.

On my first trip I saw no *palaemon*. The appearance-dates of this species in Scotland can cover a very long period; eg. from 10 May to 7 July, caused by climate conditions from year to year. I think I was too early on my first effort. On my second visit I saw many *palaemon* at the well-known Inverness-shire loch site.

My third visit was to the village of Torlundy, 4 miles north-east of Fort William, on 25 June 1966. I had been told I might well see *palaemon* on the edges of woodland, near the village school. Full of confidence, I approached the promised land. In bright sunshine I searched the area from 10.00 am to 1.00 pm without seeing *palaemon*. However, the Small Pearl Bordered Fritillary, *A. selene*, was plentiful and I had the pleasure of seeing several of the Scots form of the Argent and Sable, *Rheumaptera hastata nigrescens*, flying beside the railway line. There are many 'butterfly people', who take small notice of moths. They miss a great deal of fun! As regards *palaemon*, I was probably, yet again, too late. It really pays anyone, going all this way north, to take the trouble to find out the state of the season.

I conclude my remarks on this interesting butterfly by drawing attention to the fact that *palaemon* is a holarctic species and is found, looking very similar to our butterfly, as far afield as the Rocky Mountains in North America. Can it be that England is never again to see its darting flight down a flowery, woodland ride? I pray that contrived re-introduction is not employed. If it returns, let it come on its own wings.

So, on the appropriate word 'wings', I end this chapter and this book.

Appendix

Ser No	Species	Ovum	Larva	Pupa	Imago	Page
	APPENDIX Showing the form in which British NATIVE BUTTERFLIES pass the Winter					
1	Speckled Wood *P. aegeria*		X	X		42
2	Wall Butterfly *L. megera*		X			43
3	Mountain Ringlet *E. epiphron*		X			33
4	Scotch Argus *E. aethiops*		X			34
5	Marbled White *M. galathea*		X			44
6	Grayling *E. semele*		X			43
7	Gate-Keeper *M. tithonus*		X			40
8	Meadow Brown *M. jurtina*		X			32
9	Small Heath *C. pamphilus*		X			39
10	Large Heath *C. tullia*		X			34
11	Ringlet *A. hyperanthus*		X			39
12	Small Pearl-Bordered Fritillary *B. selene*		X			15
13	Pearl-Bordered Fritillary *B. Euphrosyne*		X			15
14	Dark Green Fritillary *M. aglaia*		X			8
15	High Brown Fritillary *A. adippe*	X				6
16	Silver-washed Fritillary *A. paphia*		X			3
17	Marsh Fritillary *E. aurinia*		X			13
18	Glanville Fritillary *M. cinxia*		X			8
19	Heath Fritillary *M. athalia*		X			11
20	Small Tortoiseshell *A. urtica*				X	91
21	Peacock *N. io*				X	83

120

Ser No	Species	Ovum	Larva	Pupa	Imago	Page
	APPENDIX Showing the form in which British NATIVE BUTTERFLIES pass the Winter					
22	Comma *P. c-album*				X	85
23	Purple Emperor *A. iris*		X			18
24	White Admiral *L. camilla*		X			86
25	Duke of Burgundy Fritillary *H. lucina*			X		16
26	Small Blue *C. minimus*		X			67
27	Silver-Studded Blue *P. argus*	X				52
28	Brown Argus *A. agestes*	X				54
29	Mountain Argus *A. artaxerxes*	X				55
30	Common Blue *P. icarus*	X				65
31	Chalk-Hill Blue *L. coridon*	X				62
32	Adonis Blue *L. bellargus*		X			64
33	Large Blue *M. arion*		X			56
34	Holly Blue *C. argiolus*			X		66
35	Small Copper *L. phlaeas*		X			67
36	Green Hairstreak *C. rubi*	X				73
37	Brown Hairstreak *T. betulae*	X				75
38	Purple Hairstreak *T. quercus*	X				74
39	White-Letter Hairstreak *S. w-album*	X				78
40	Black Hairstreak *S. pruni*	X				79
41	Swallow-Tail *P. machaon*			X		46
42	Large White *P. brassicae*			X		97

121

Ser No	Species	Ovum	Larva	Pupa	Imago	Page
	APPENDIX Showing the form in which British NATIVE BUTTERFLIES pass the Winter					
43	Small White *P. rapae*			X		99
44	Green-Veined White *P. napi*			X		100
45	Orange-Tip *A. cardamines*			X		101
46	Brimstone *G. rhamni*				X	94
47	Wood White *L. sinapis*			X		102
48	Grizzled Skipper *P. malvae*			X		105
49	Dingy Skipper *E. tages*			X		104
50	Small Skipper *T. sylvestris*	X				105
51	Essex Skipper *T. lineola*	X				105
52	Lulworth Skipper *T. acteon*	X				107
53	Silver-Spotted Skipper *H. comma*	X				108
54	Large Skipper *O. venata*		X			108
55	Chequered Skipper *C. palaemon*		X			110
	TOTALS	15	26	11	4	

Bibliography

British Butterflies, by W.S. Coleman, April 1860

A History of British Butterflies, by Rev F.O. Morris, 1893

Butterflies of the British Isles, by Richard South, 1921

Natural History of British Butterflies, by F.W. Frohawk, 1924

Butterflies, by E.B. Ford, 1946

'Heredity' Vol 22, 1967

The Butterflies of Scotland, A Natural History, by George Thomson, 1980

A Field Guide to the Butterflies of Britain and Europe, by L.G. Higgins & N.D. Riley, 1984

The Butterflies of Britain and Ireland, by Jeremy Thomas and Richard Lewington, 1991

The Proceedings of the British Entomological & Natural History Society. Published quarterly

The Entomologists Record and Journal of Variation Published monthly

Index

A
Abbot's Wood   12
Albin's Eye   53
Andover   12,13,17
Andover Natural History
   Society   77
andronica   104-105
 anticaecastriata postfulvescens 64
April Fritillary 15

B
Barton Stacey   17
B.E.N.H.S.   39,96,112
Beaconsfield   36
Bittern   48
Black-throated Diver   48
Black Redstart   111
Blean Wood   12
Blomer, Captain   53
Borth Bog   38
Bretherton, R.F.   37
Brock, Mrs Helen   40
Bude   61
Burning Cliff   108
Buttermere Fell   34

C
Cark-in-Cartmel   35
Castle Eden Dene Argus   55
Castor Hanglands   110
Catfield Common   46
Chilterns   110
Cirl Bunting   41, 109
Coleman, W.S.   59, 99, 107
Cotley Hill   44

Crowthorne   1
Cuillin Hills   37

D
Dale, JC   9, 107
Dotted Rustic   84
Dowdeswell, W.H.   32, 33
Dulverton   62
Dulwich   9
Dunsfold Wood   102
Durdle Door   107

F
Fenn's Moss   35
Fenn's Wainscot   35
Ford, E.B.   5, 9, 12, 32, 34,
   37, 39, 40, 46, 52, 55, 107
Foulness   106
Frowhawk, F.W.   57
Evans, Miss Ethel   115
Fyfield   10

G
Ghost Moth   92
Glanville, Mrs Margaret   9
Glen Brittle   37
Glenshian   115
Great Auk   114
Great Bedwyn   11
Great Orme's Head   43
Grovely Wood   16

H
Harewood Forest   6, 21, 78
Harris, Moses   9

125

Hobby   110
Holbeach   80, 81
Holkar   35
Howarth, T.G.   60
Huia, The   56
Hutchinson, Miss E.   85
Hyssington   86

I
Isle of Mull   13
Isle of Wight   8, 93
Irish Jay   100

J
Joycey, James   115

K
Kirkcaldy, Lt-Col. Sam   6, 7, 108

L
Lake Bala   37
Large Tortoiseshell   16
Lewis Spedan   50
Lipscomb, Maj-Gen. D.G.   16, 21, 45, 63, 64, 79, 102
Llanbrynmair   73
Lodge, John   60, 69, 71
Longmoor Point   46
Longparish   6
Lukis, Rev. J. W.   9, 11
Lulworth Cove   107.

M
Machynlleth   38
Mackworth-Praed, Lt-Col. D. W.   116
Marlborough College   1
Marrakech   93
masseyi   53, 54
Maxwell, Sir Reginald   77
McWhirter, Kennedy   32

Middle Wallop   106
Monk's Wood   79, 82
morphos 65
Morris, Rev. F. O.   9, 10, 18, 41, 47, 59, 100, 110
Moss, J. E.   98
myrmica 59
Myxomatosis 60

N
Napley, Sir David   55
Nature Conservancy H.Q.   79
New Forest   43, 75, 84
New Forest Burnet   113
New Zealand   56
Northern Footman   36

O
Operation 'Veritable'
Old Lady   84

P
Painted Lady   92
Passenger Pigeon   114
Peterborough Cathedral   111
Porter, Jim   87
Porton   109
Potsdam   1
Prince Albert   1
Purefoy, E. B.   58

R
Robertson-Justice, James   81
Rock-eyed Underwing   44
Rockingham Forest   113
Royal Scottish Museum   115
Russwurm, A. D. A.   45

S
'Saki'   74
Salcey Forest   112
Salisbury Plain   8, 14, 16, 74

126

Scarce Forester   44
Scott, Sir Peter   62, 81, 82
Shoeburyness   106
Silky Wave   53
Skinner, Bernard   35
Skye   37, 39
Sobers, Sir Garfield   54
South, Richard   5, 14, 47, 59
Starling, Mr   47
St. Catherine's Mount   14, 73
Stockbridge Down   8
Stone Curlew   109
Sutton Broad   46

T

Thomas, Dr Jeremy   71
Thomson, George   115
Thrislington   55
Tidworth   77
Torlundy   116
Tottenham   8

V

valezina   5
Von Moltke   58

W

Weavers' Fritillary   53
Wellington College   1
Wester Ross   48
Whiteparish   20, 22
Whitby, Dr Jim   10, 12, 13,
   46, 47, 48
Whitlock, Mr   47
Whixall Moss   36
Woodlark   91
Worms, Baron de   11, 59, 61,
   112

Z

Zygaena lonicerae jocelynae
   (Trem) 37